National Research
Council Canada

Conseil national
de recherches Canada

KT-199-521

Glossary of Permafrost and Related Ground-Ice Terms

Permafrost Subcommittee
Associate Committee on Geotechnical Research
National Research Council of Canada

Prepared by: S.A. Harris, H.M. French, J.A. Heginbottom,
G.H. Johnston, B. Ladanyi, D.C. Sego, R.O. van Everdingen
National Research Council of Canada
Ottawa, Ontario, Canada K1A 0R6

Technical Memorandum No. 142

ISBN 0-660-12540-4
NRCC 27952
Technical Memorandum No. 142

Aussi disponible en français

Cover photo: oblique aerial view of low-centre *polygons* on a river terrace north of Raddi Lake, southwestern Banks Island, N.W.T. (Photo by J.S. Vincent, Geological Survey of Canada)

DRD
C

89   09039

Table of Contents

Preface

Permafrost, or perennially cryotic ground, refers to ground (i.e., soil and rock) that remains at or below 0°C for at least two years. In Canada, permafrost is found beneath approximately 50 per cent of the land surface, and the remainder of the country is affected by seasonal frost and ground freezing to varying degrees. Only the U.S.S.R. has a larger permafrost region than Canada, although large areas of Alaska, the People's Republic of China, Greenland, northern Scandinavia and Antarctica are also underlain by permafrost.

The last 20 years have witnessed a dramatic increase in economic activities in northern Canada, largely associated with the search for energy resources, notably oil and natural gas. With this development and the need for associated infrastructure has come a growing appreciation of the problems caused by ground freezing, seasonal frost and permafrost. Such problems have long been recognized in the Soviet Union where geocryological studies are well established. In North America permafrost science and permafrost engineering are rapidly growing academic disciplines with strong applied relevance.

In 1974, a booklet entitled *Permafrost Terminology*, prepared by the late R.J.E. Brown and W.O. Kupsch, was published under the sponsorship of the Permafrost Subcommittee, Associate Committee on Geotechnical Research, National Research Council of Canada. The first of its kind in Canada, this glossary of terms related to permafrost was compiled in response to the growing need for standardized terminology caused by the great increase in permafrost scientific and engineering investigations in Canada.

At a meeting of the Permafrost Subcommittee in October 1982, it was recommended that *Permafrost Terminology* be updated and reissued. A survey of permafrost experts in North America conducted by the subcommittee confirmed the need to expand the existing list of terms to include, for example, pertinent engineering and ground-ice terms, and to make appropriate changes to reflect current usage. In 1983, to prepare and publish this new Glossary, the subcommittee established a working group, which consisted of Professor S.A. Harris, Chairman, Professor H.M. French, Mr. J.A. Heginbottom, Mr. G.H. Johnston, Professor B. Ladanyi, Professor D.C. Sego and Dr. R.O. van Everdingen. The present volume is the result of three years of regular meetings of the working group. A French translation of the Glossary has been prepared.

On behalf of the Associate Committee on Geotechnical Research, I wish to thank the individuals involved for the tremendous time, effort and intellectual endeavour they have devoted to this publication. I believe the Glossary will be of great value and will receive widespread use in Canada. If it were to be adopted elsewhere in the world, the National Research Council of Canada would be delighted to have played a role.

V. Milligan
Chairman
Associate Committee on Geotechnical Research

Acknowledgements

The working group gratefully acknowledges the assistance of those people who provided comments on the terms during the preparation of the Glossary. Comments on the first list of terms proposed for inclusion in the Glossary and on the first draft of the definitions, commentary and references finally selected, were received from: M. Allard, Centre d'Études Nordiques, Université Laval; T.H.W. Baker, Institute for Research in Construction, National Research Council Canada; J. Brown, U.S. Army, Cold Regions Research and Engineering Laboratory; O.J. Ferrians, U.S. Geological Survey; L.E. Goodrich, Institute for Research in Construction, National Research Council Canada; W.O. Kupsch, Department of Geological Sciences, University of Saskatchewan; J.R. Mackay, Department of Geography, University of British Columbia; J.D. Mollard, J.D. Mollard and Associates, Ltd., T.E. Osterkamp, Geophysical Institute, University of Alaska; T.L. Péwé, Department of Geology, Arizona State University; V.N. Rampton, Terrain Analysis and Mapping Services, Ltd.; L. Samson, Terratech Ltd.; P.V. Sellmann, U.S. Army, Cold Regions Research and Engineering Laboratory; M.W. Smith, Department of Geography, Carleton University; W. Stanek, Canadian Forestry Service, Environment Canada; A.L. Washburn, Quaternary Research Centre, University of Washington; J.R. Williams, U.S. Geological Survey; P.J. Williams, Geotechnical Science Laboratories, Carleton University; S.C. Zoltai, Canadian Forestry Service, Environment Canada.

Mrs. C.A. Gustafson, University of Calgary, carried out a literature search and ably assisted the working group in preparing an initial list of terms for inclusion in the Glossary.

The assistance and co-operation received from the Publications Section, and especially Linda Hayes, and the Graphics Unit, Institute for Research in Construction, National Research Council Canada are gratefully acknowledged. Sincere thanks and appreciation must be expressed to Mrs. N.E. Hardy, Institute for Research in Construction, National Research Council Canada for the many hours and special effort given in typing the many drafts and the final manuscript for the Glossary.

Permission received from those who provided illustrations is greatly appreciated; acknowledgement of the original source is given in the figure captions.

The continued interest and expert assistance given by Mrs. Penny Williams of PMF Editorial Services Inc., and Mrs. Judith Gregory of Gregory Gregory Limited are gratefully acknowledged.

Introduction

This Glossary is not intended to be an encylopaedia concerning the permafrost regions of Canada. Rather it is a list of definitions* related to permafrost science and permafrost engineering. The primary objective is to present terms that enjoy common usage in the current literature, with special reference to Canada and Canadian conditions. The Glossary is based upon *Permafrost Terminology*, a booklet published in December 1974 by the late R.J.E. Brown and W.O. Kupsch. There are, however, several important differences between the present volume and its predecessor.

First, the scope of this volume is wider. Although most entries relate directly to the features and processes occurring in permafrost areas, including those related to ground ice, frost action, freezing, thawing and periglacial phenomena, other entries are included because of their importance in permafrost regions even though they are not unique to permafrost regions. This volume also includes as many ground-ice and engineering terms relevant to frozen ground as possible.

Second, a significant change from the original work is this Glossary's attempt to resolve a major semantic problem in permafrost terminology involving the use of the word "frozen." As noted by Brown and Kupsch, some permafrost workers "contended that 'frozen' should be used to refer to earth materials below 0°C whether or not water (in the solid and possibly liquid state) is present." Others "believed that earth materials should not be considered as 'frozen' unless they contain ice." It is important to note that the terms *frozen ground* and *unfrozen ground* are defined in this volume to differentiate between ground (soil and rock) that is at a temperature of 0°C or below and contains ice, and ground that is at a temperature of 0°C or below but does not contain ice. Wherever possible, geocryological terminology has been adopted. In addition, it is recommended that the adjectives "cryotic" and "noncryotic" be used to refer solely to the temperature of the material described, independent of its water and/or ice content.

The definition for the term *permafrost* in this Glossary remains essentially the same as in *Permafrost Terminology*. It is defined on the basis of temperature. However, as pointed out in the commentary for this term, "...whereas all perennially frozen ground is *permafrost*, not all *permafrost* is perennially frozen," because the ground, although at a temperature below 0°C (i.e., cryotic) may not contain ice.

---

*Italic type has been used throughout to denote that a word or term is defined in the glossary. The only exceptions to this are "ice" and "permafrost" because they appear so frequently.

A third departure from *Permafrost Terminology* is that since the Glossary is intended primarily to assist Canadian permafrost scientists and engineers working in northern Canada, North American, English-language terms are used wherever possible. Transliteration from European, Russian and Chinese literature has been avoided as far as possible; foreign-language terms are included only if they are well established in English usage (e.g., *alas; talik*). Preference has been given to widely used English-language terms, if available (e.g., *icing* rather than "aufeis"). In all cases, the main concern is with current usage rather than original definitions and past usage.

Fourth, this Glossary is considerably larger than *Permafrost Terminology*. Definitions are provided for 201 of the 596 terms listed. Certain terms are identified as "not recommended" for a number of reasons: to clarify thought and to achieve more precise language; to standardize terminology; to avoid the use of transliterations; and to emphasize widely-used English equivalents. It is the hope of the working group that these "not recommended" terms will disappear from lack of use by permafrost workers in Canada and elsewhere. In addition, adjectival words such as "fossil," which have their origin in the Pleistocene periglacial and stratigraphic literature, are inappropriate in the context of current permafrost regions which can possess both active and inactive (sic, "fossil") forms and processes. For this reason, terms such as *pingo scar* and *ice-wedge cast* are terms recommended in the Glossary.

In addition to the 201 defined terms, the list contains a number of inverse word order listings to achieve alphabetical groupings of related terms. Thus, the "ice" terms, such as *aggradational ice* and *buried ice*, are listed as *ice, aggradational* and *ice, buried*, and the "permafrost" terms, such as *alpine permafrost* and *epigenetic permafrost*, are listed as *permafrost, alpine* and *permafrost, epigenetic*. The alphabetic order of the glossary is word by word rather than letter by letter, and recognizes punctuation, i.e., inverse terms such as *permafrost, dry,* precedes *permafrost boundary*. The French equivalent, when there is one, is found within square brackets below the English defined term. This procedure is reversed in the French language edition. The remaining terms in the Glossary are either cross referenced to, or are considered acceptable synonyms for, the defined terms. Some of these latter terms are included within major groups under main headings, e.g., *patterned ground, solifluction features, taliks,* etc.

The references, an essential part of the Glossary, provide the user with a source list from which to obtain more detailed information and to understand the historical development of certain permafrost concepts. For the most part, references have been restricted to either classic, "bench mark" or pioneer papers, or to those which are up to date, informative and easily accessible in North America. As far as possible, Canadian examples and experience have been referenced. The reference list is *not* intended to be comprehensive.

Diagrams and photographs have been included in the Glossary in order to illustrate conceptual ideas and terminology, and to help differentiate between certain permafrost phenomena. It is not the intent that all permafrost phenomena be illustrated in the Glossary, just as the Glossary is not meant to be a textbook.

The working group is aware that not all permafrost workers will agree with the approach adopted or, indeed, all the definitions listed. Comments and suggestions concerning terms, definitions and format are welcome. Please send your comments to:

> Research Advisor
> Permafrost Subcommittee
> Associate Committee on Geotechnical Research
> National Research Council Canada
> Ottawa, Ontario
> Canada K1A 0R6

It is the firm belief of the working group that the Glossary summarizes many important advances in our understanding of permafrost in North America, and its standardized list of terms and concepts will assist in the future growth of permafrost science and engineering.

Working Group on the Permafrost Glossary

Professor S.A. Harris
Department of Geography
The University of Calgary
Calgary, Alberta
T2N 1N4

Professor H.M. French
Departments of Geography and Geology
University of Ottawa
Ottawa, Ontario
K1N 6N5

Mr. J.A. Heginbottom
Geological Survey of Canada
601 Booth Street
Ottawa, Ontario
K1A 0E8

Mr. G.H. Johnston
Geotechnical Section
Institute for Research in Construction
National Research Council Canada
Ottawa, Ontario
K1A 0R6

Professor B. Ladanyi
Département de génie civil
Université de Montréal
Ecole Polytechnique
C.P. 6079 - Succ. "A"
Montréal, Québec
H3C 3A7

Dr. D.C. Sego
Department of Civil Engineering
University of Alberta
Edmonton, Alberta
T6G 2G7

Dr. R.O. van Everdingen
The Arctic Institute of North America
University of Calgary
Calgary, Alberta
T2N 1N4

A

acoustically-defined permafrost (see *permafrost, ice-bonded*[1])

active frost (not recommended; see *frost, seasonal*)

active ice wedge (see *ice wedge*)

active layer (see also *depth of thaw; frost, seasonal; permafrost, seasonally active; residual thaw layer; seasonally frozen ground; seasonally thawed ground*)
[mollisol]
The top layer of ground subject to annual thawing and freezing in areas underlain by permafrost (see Figure 2).

> COMMENT: The thickness of the active layer varies from year to year, depending on such factors as the ambient air temperature, vegetation, drainage, soil or rock type and water content, snow cover, and degree and orientation of slope. As a rule, it is thin in the High Arctic (15 cm or less) and becomes thicker farther south (1 m or more). In the zone of *continuous permafrost* it generally reaches the *permafrost table*. In the zone of *discontinuous permafrost* it often does not.
> The active layer includes the uppermost part of the permafrost wherever either the salinity or clay content of the permafrost allows it to thaw and refreeze annually, even though the material remains cryotic (below 0°C).
> The active layer is sometimes referred to as the "active zone"; the term "zone," however, should be reserved for the zones of *discontinuous* and *continuous permafrost*. Use of the term "depth to permafrost" as a synonym for the thickness of the active layer is misleading, especially in areas where the active layer is separated from the permafrost by a *residual thaw layer*, that is, by a thawed or noncryotic (above 0°C) layer of ground.
> REFERENCES: Müller, 1943; Williams, 1965; Brown, 1971; van Everdingen, 1985.

active layer, relict
[paléomollisol]
A layer of ground, now perennially frozen, lying immediately below the modern active layer. Its thickness indicates the greater annual *depth of thaw* that occurred during a previous, warmer climatic period.

> COMMENT: The base of the relict active layer is a thaw unconformity, which may be recognized by differences in *ice contents*, stable isotope contents, and heavy mineral and pollen assemblages above and below the unconformity, and by the truncation of ice bodies.
> REFERENCES: Delorme et al., 1978; Mackay, 1978.

---

[1]Terms in italic are defined elsewhere in the Glossary.

active-layer failure (see also *detachment failure*)
      [rupture de mollisol]
A general term referring to several forms of slope failures or failure mechanisms commonly occurring in areas underlain by permafrost (see Figure 21a).

> COMMENT: These include *detachment failures* but not *retrogressive thaw slumps* and *thaw slumping* since these involve permafrost.
> SYNONYM: (not recommended) skin flow.

active-layer glide (not recommended; see *active-layer failure; detachment failure*)

active method of construction (see *construction methods in permafrost*)

active rock glacier (see *rock glacier*)

active thermokarst (see *thermokarst terrain*)

active zone (not recommended; see *active layer*)

adfreeze/adfreezing (see also *strength, adfreeze*)
      [congélation adhérente]
The process by which two objects are bonded together by ice formed between them during the freezing of water.
> COMMENT: One of the objects may be ice.
> SYNONYM: frost grip.
> REFERENCE: Muller, 1943.

adfreezing force (not recommended; see *strength, adfreeze*)

adfreeze strength (see *strength, adfreeze*)

aggradation of permafrost (see *permafrost aggradation*)

aggradational ice (see *ice, aggradational*)

air freezing/thawing index (see *freezing index; thawing index;* see also *n-factor*)

alas/alass (see also *thermokarst*)
      [alass]
A depression found in *thermokarst terrain*, produced by thawing of
extensive areas of very thick and exceedingly *ice-rich permafrost*.

> COMMENT: Typically, alasses are large depressions ranging from 0.5
> to more than 100 km² in area and from 5 to 20 m in depth. In the early
> stages of formation, a shallow (< 2 m) circular "alas lake" forms in a
> steep-sided depression. Enlargement and ultimate drainage of a number
> of such lakes produce low interalas plateaus (termed "mezhalasye" in
> Russian). Ultimately, the plateaus disappear and *mass wasting* produces
> gentle side slopes. The term is of Yakut origin.
> REFERENCES: Czudek and Demek, 1970; Soloviev, 1973.

alpine permafrost (see *permafrost, alpine*)

altiplanation terrace (not recommended; see *cryoplanation terrace*)

annual frost zone (not recommended; see *active layer*)

annually frozen/thawed layer (not recommended; see *active layer*)

apparent heat capacity (see *thermal properties of frozen ground*)

aquiclude, cryogenic (see *cryogenic aquiclude*)

aufeis (not recommended; see *icing*)

B

basal cryopeg (see *cryopeg*)

basal heave (see *frost heave*)

base of permafrost (see *permafrost base*)

baydzherakh (not recommended; see *mound, thermokarst*)

beaded channel (see *beaded stream*)

beaded drainage (not recommended; see *beaded stream*)

beaded stream

[cours d'eau en chapelet]

A stream characterized by narrow reaches linking pools or small lakes (see Figure 22a).

> COMMENT: A characteristic pattern of small streams in areas underlain by *ice wedges*. The course of the stream channel is controlled by the pattern of the wedges, with the beads (pools) occurring at the junctions of the wedges. When the intervening channels are dry, they may be called "beaded channels."
> SYNONYMS: (not recommended) beaded drainage, button drainage.
> REFERENCES: Péwé, 1954; Hopkins et al., 1955; Ferrians et al., 1969; Brown, 1970b; Lawson and Brown, 1978.

biennially frozen ground (not recommended; see *permafrost*)

bimodal flow (not recommended; see *retrogressive thaw slump*)

block field

[champ de blocs]

A surficial layer of angular shattered rocks formed in either modern or Pleistocene periglacial environments.

> SYNONYMS: stone field and (not recommended) felsenmeer, blockmeer.
> REFERENCES: French, 1976; Washburn, 1979.

bog, string (see *string fen*)

boulder field (not recommended; see *block field*)

bugor (not recommended; see *frost mound*)

bulgunniakh (not recommended; see *frost mound; pingo*)

buried ice (see *ice, buried*)

button drainage (not recommended; see *beaded stream*)

C

cave ice (see *ice, cave*)

cave-in lake (not recommended; see *thermokarst lake*; see also *thermokarst terrain*)

cemetery mound (not recommended; see *mound, thermokarst*)

chrystocrene/crystocrene (not recommended; see *icing*)

circle, nonsorted/sorted (see *patterned ground*)

climafrost (not recommended; see *permafrost*; see also *pereletok*)

closed-cavity ice (see *ice, closed-cavity*)

closed-system freezing (see *freezing, closed-system*)

closed-system pingo (see *pingo, closed-system*)

closed talik (see *talik*)

collapse scar (see also *thermokarst terrain*)
   [cicatrice d'affaissement]
That portion of a *peatland* where the whole or part of a *palsa* or *peat plateau* has thawed and collapsed to the level of the surrounding *peatland* (see figures 14 and 15e).
> COMMENT: A collapse scar is not a depression but is marked by vegetation different from the wetland that did not contain permafrost. Irregular topography (hence *thermokarst terrain*) may be present on the *peatland* as a whole but the collapse scars are only part of that *thermokarst terrain*, marked by the absence of permafrost, and by vegetation different from that on both the previously unfrozen *peatlands* and the remnant permafrost peat landforms.
> REFERENCE: Zoltai, 1971.

collapsed pingo (see *pingo*)

composite wedge (see also *ice wedge; ice-wedge cast; sand wedge; soil wedge*)

[fente en coin à remplissage composé]

A wedge showing evidence of both primary and secondary filling.

COMMENT: When used with reference to *thermal contraction crack* phenomena in permafrost, it describes a wedge filled by a combination of ice and soil (usually sand). The term is most frequently used to describe Pleistocene *sand wedges* and *ice-wedge casts*. Sand wedges are wedges of primary filling since, at the time of their formation, they are filled with mineral soil. Upon thawing of the permafrost, there is little or no void space left, and any subsequent downward movement of material into the wedge is negligible.

By contrast, *ice-wedge casts* are wedges of secondary filling. When the permafrost thaws, the *ice wedge* melts and the enclosing and overlying sediments collapse into the trough. Typically, composite wedges are filled with material very similar in structure and texture to sands in a typical fissure of primary filling (i.e., *sand wedge*). However, there may be inclusions of material from the fissure walls and some distortion of the adjacent sediments bordering the wedge, reflecting the presence of ice in the original fill material.

REFERENCES: Black and Berg, 1966; Gozdzik, 1973; French, 1976; Washburn, 1979.

conductance, electrical (see *electrical properties of frozen ground*)

conductivity, thermal (see *thermal properties of frozen ground*)

congelifluction (not recommended; see *gelifluction*)

congelifraction (see *frost wedging*)

congeliturbate/congeliturbation (not recommended; see *cryoturbate; cryoturbation*)

consolidation, thaw (see *thaw consolidation*)

construction methods in permafrost

[construction dans le pergélisol, méthodes de]

Special design and construction procedures required when engineering works are undertaken in permafrost areas.

COMMENT: Design and construction of engineering works on permafrost normally follow one of two broad principles which are based on whether or not the frozen foundation soil or rock is thaw-stable or thaw-unstable (*thaw-sensitive permafrost*).

Permafrost conditions can be neglected, and conventional designs and construction methods used when foundation materials are stable upon thawing. When the foundation materials are thaw-sensitive, however, then either the "passive" or "active" design and construction method is selected.

The passive method maintains the foundation materials in a frozen state. Preservation of the frozen condition or *permafrost aggradation* can be accomplished using *thermal piles* or *thermosyphons*, or by using either a ventilation or an insulation construction technique; often a combination of these techniques is used.

The ventilation technique requires that there is a clear space left between the bottom of the structure and the ground surface, or that the structure is placed on a fill pad with ducts incorporated in the pad or the floor system. Movement of cold air through the air space or ducts dissipates heat from the structure above and removes heat from the ground below.

Using the insulation technique, a relatively thick fill (sometimes containing a layer of insulation) is placed on the ground surface to prevent thawing or to reduce or control the *depth of thaw* below the original ground surface.

When *permafrost degradation* cannot be prevented, then the active method must be considered. Two main approaches are possible. Unfavourable foundation materials are thawed and compacted or else they are replaced with more suitable materials before the structure is erected. Alternatively, the foundations and structure are designed to accommodate the *thaw settlements* that will occur.

REFERENCES: Andersland and Anderson, 1978; Linell and Lobacz, 1980; Johnston, 1981.

contemporary permafrost (see *permafrost, equilibrium*)

continuous permafrost (see *permafrost, continuous*)

continuous permafrost zone (see *permafrost, continuous*; see also *permafrost zone*)

contraction crack (not recommended; see *thermal contraction crack*)

creep of frozen ground (see also *frost creep*)
    [fluage du gélisol]
The slow deformation that results from long-term application of a stress too small to produce failure in the frozen material.

COMMENT: In frozen soils, creep deformations are due mainly to the creep of *pore ice* and the migration of unfrozen *pore water*. In ice-saturated frozen soils, most creep deformations are distortional with little or no volume change. In frozen soils with large *unfrozen water contents* or in unsaturated frozen soils, slow deformations due to consolidation, and creep due to volume change, may also occur. Usually, a large portion of the creep deformation is permanent.
REFERENCES: Vyalov, 1959; Ladanyi, 1972, 1981.

creep, frost (see *frost creep*)

critical ice content (not recommended; see *ice content*)

critical water content (not recommended; see *water content, total*)

cryic layer (not recommended; see *permafrost*)

cryoatmosphere (see *cryosphere*)

cryoepigenesis (see *cryogenesis*)

cryofront (see also *freezing front*)
    [cryofront]
The boundary between *cryotic* and *noncryotic ground* as indicated by the position of the 0°C isotherm in the ground (see figures 4 and 5).
> COMMENT: The *permafrost base* and the boundaries between noncryotic and cryotic portions of the *active layer* constitute cryofronts. As a result of *freezing-point depression*, the *freezing front* usually lags behind the cryofront as it moves downwards during annual freezing of the *active layer*.
> REFERENCE: van Everdingen, 1976.

cryogenesis
    [cryogenèse]
The combination of thermophysical, physico-chemical and physico-mechanical processes occurring in freezing, frozen and thawing earth materials.
> COMMENT: This term is frequently used in the Russian permafrost literature. Specific processes of cryogenesis include water migration during freezing and thawing of the ground, *frost heave*, heat and mass (moisture) exchange, regelation and *gelifluction*.
> REFERENCE: Poppe and Brown, 1976.

cryogenic aquiclude
    [aquiclude cryogénique]
A layer of ground which, because of its frozen state, has a low enough permeability to act as a confining bed for an underlying aquifer.
> COMMENT: Annual freezing can turn the *active layer* into a cryogenic aquiclude.
> REFERENCE: Fotiev, 1978.

cryogenic fabric (see also *cryosol*)

[microstructure cryogénique]

The distinct soil micromorphology resulting from the effects of freezing and thawing processes (see Figure 8).

COMMENT: The following cryogenic fabrics can be distinguished under a microscope:

1. granic and granoidic fabrics – soil particles form discrete loosely packed units. These fabrics are generally attributed to freeze-thaw processes and the formation of *needle ice* near the ground surface.
2. fragmic and fragmoidal fabrics – soil particles form discrete units that are either densely packed or coalescing. These fabrics commonly occur in subsurface soil horizons, usually close to the *freezing front* where soil material is subject to *ice lens* formation.
3. banded and isoband fabrics – soil particles form subhorizontal layers which result from freeze-thaw processes accompanied by eluviation.
4. orbiculic, suscitic and conglomeric fabrics – coarser soil particles form circular to ellipsoidal patterns (orbiculic), vertical or near-vertical orientation (suscitic), and compound arrangements (conglomeric), probably as a result of *cryoturbation* activity.

REFERENCES: Brewer and Pawluk, 1975; Pawluk and Brewer, 1975; Fox, 1983.

cryogenic mound (not recommended; see *frost mound*)

cryogenic soil (see *cryosol*)

cryogenic structure (not recommended; see *cryostructure*)

cryogenic suction (not recommended; see *cryosuction*)

cryogenic temperature

[température cryogénique]

In international materials science, this term refers to temperatures generally below -50°C, but usually to temperatures within a few degrees of absolute zero (-273°C). In the Russian permafrost literature, this term refers to temperatures below 0°C.

cryogenic texture (not recommended; see *cryotexture*)

cryogenic weathering (see *frost weathering*)

cryohydrosphere (see *cryosphere*)

cryokarst (not recommended; see *thermokarst*)

cryolaccolith (not recommended; see *frost blister; ice, intrusive; pingo*)

cryolithology (see also *geocryology*)
    [cryolithologie]
The study of the genesis, structure and lithology of earth materials having temperatures below 0°C.
> COMMENT: This is a Russian term not widely used in North America. It is a branch of *geocryology* in which lithological and *ground-ice* conditions are emphasized.

cryolithosphere (see *cryosphere*)

cryology (not recommended; see *geocryology*)

cryomorphic soil (not recommended; see *cryosol*)

cryopedology (see also *cryosol; geocryology*)
    [cryopédologie]
The study of soils (the solum) at temperatures below 0°C, with particular reference to soils subject to intensive *frost action* and to soils overlying permafrost.
> COMMENT: As originally defined (Bryan, 1946), the term comprised the whole science of *geocryology*, including the civil engineering methods used to overcome difficulties resulting from intensive *frost action* and the existence of permafrost.
> REFERENCES: Bryan, 1946; Canada Soil Survey Committee, 1978.

cryopeg (see also *permafrost, saline; talik*)
    [cryopeg]
A layer of *unfrozen ground* that is perennially cryotic (forming part of the permafrost), in which freezing is prevented by *freezing-point depression* due to the dissolved-solids content of the *pore water* (see figures 2, 4 and 11).
> COMMENT: Three types of cryopeg can be distinguished on the basis of their position with respect to permafrost:
> 1. a basal cryopeg forms the basal portion of the permafrost;
> 2. an isolated cryopeg is entirely surrounded by perennially *frozen ground;*
> 3. a marine cryopeg is found in coastal or subsea perennially *frozen ground.*
>
> REFERENCE: Tolstikhin and Tolstikhin, 1974.

cryoplanation terrace
[terrasse d'altiplanation]
A step-like or table-like bench cut in bedrock in cold climate regions.
> COMMENT: Cryoplanation terraces may occur as both hillside benches or bevelled summit surfaces and often lack structural control. They are thought to form under conditions of intense *frost wedging* associated with snowbanks. Cryoplanation terraces are more frequently reported from continental *periglacial* areas of moderate aridity. As these areas are usually underlain by permafrost, cryoplanation terraces are regarded by some as diagnostic landforms of permafrost terrain.
> REFERENCES: Eakin, 1916; Demek, 1969; French, 1976; Reger and Péwé, 1976; Washburn, 1979.

cryosol (see also *cryogenic fabric; cryopedology; cryoturbation; geocryology*)
[cryosol]
Soil formed in either mineral or organic materials having permafrost either within 1 m of the surface or, if the soil is strongly cryoturbated, within 2 m of the surface, and having a mean annual soil temperature below 0°C.
> COMMENT: This is a a pedological term for a major soil order. Cryosolic soils are divided into three groups:
> 1. turbic cryosols developed on mineral soils and strongly cryoturbated;
> 2. static cryosols developed on mineral soils but with little or no cryoturbation;
> 3. organic cryosols developed on organic (peat) materials.
> SYNONYMS: (not recommended) cryosolic soil, pergelic soil.
> REFERENCE: Canada Soil Survey Committee, 1978.

cryosolic soil (not recommended; see *cryosol*)

cryosphere (see also *permafrost region*)
[cryosphère]
That part of the earth's crust and atmosphere subject to temperatures below 0°C for at least part of each year.
> COMMENT: The cryosphere may be divided into the cryoatmosphere, the cryohydrosphere and the cryolithosphere. Some authorities exclude the earth's atmosphere from the cryosphere; others restrict the term "cryosphere" to the regions of the earth's crust where permafrost exists.
> REFERENCE: Baranov, 1978.

cryostatic pressure (not recommended; see *freezing pressure*)

cryostructure (see also *cryotexture; frozen ground; ice, pore; permafrost, ice-bonded*)

[cryostructure]

The structural characteristics of frozen, fine-grained earth materials (see Figure 9).

> COMMENT: The cryostructure is determined by the amount and distribution of *pore ice* (or ice cement) and lenses of *segregated ice*. The type and arrangement of ice in the frozen material will depend largely on the initial *water content* of the material and the extent of moisture migration during subsequent freezing.
>
> For engineering purposes, the structure of frozen soil may be described as massive, layered or reticulate, based on the type and distribution of ice in the soil. A massive structure (not to be confused with massive *ground-ice* forms) is characterized by the predominant presence of *pore ice* and by a relatively low total *ice content*. In soils with a reticulate structure, *ice lenses* generally form a random net, whereas in those with a layered structure they occur as well-oriented horizontal lenses alternating with soil layers having a massive structure. In both cases their total *ice content* is relatively high.
>
> REFERENCES: U.S.S.R., 1969, 1973; Poppe and Brown, 1976; Kudryavtsev, 1978.

cryosuction (see also *frost action*)

[cryosuccion]

A suction developed as a result of freezing.

> SYNONYM: (not recommended) frost suction.
> REFERENCE: Blanchard and Frémond, 1982.

cryosyngenesis (see *cryogenesis*)

cryotexture (see also *cryostructure*)

[cryotexture]

The textural characteristics of frozen, fine-grained organic and mineral earth materials cemented together with ice.

> COMMENT: Soviet permafrost scientists identify ten "cryogenic textures," or cryotextures: massive, massive-porous, basal, basal-layered, crust-like, massive-agglomerate, lens type, lattice type, layered and lattice-block type. Cryotextures may be useful in determining the nature of the freezing process and the conditions under which the sediments accumulated.
>
> REFERENCES: Poppe and Brown, 1976; Kudryavtsev, 1978.

cryotic (see *cryotic ground*)

cryotic ground (see also *frozen ground; noncryotic ground; permafrost*)
   [sol cryotique]
Soil or rock at temperatures of 0°C or lower.

   COMMENT: The terms "cryotic" and "noncryotic" were introduced to
   solve a major semantic problem identified by Brown and Kupsch
   (1974), namely the lack of specific separate terms to designate "above
   0°C" and "below 0°C" as opposed to "unfrozen" (not containing ice)
   and "frozen" (containing ice) (see Figure 3). Cryotic and noncryotic
   refer solely to the temperature of the material described, independent of
   its water or ice content. Perennially cryotic ground refers to ground that
   remains at or below 0°C continuously for two or more years and is
   therefore synonymous with permafrost.
   REFERENCES: Brown and Kupsch, 1974; van Everdingen, 1976.

cryoturbate (see also *cryoturbation*)
   [matériaux géliturbés]
A body of unconsolidated earth material moved or disturbed by frost
action.

   COMMENT: The process of *cryoturbation* results in the disruption and
   distortion of soil horizons and structures, the formation of *patterned
   ground*, the growth of involutions, and the formation of organic-rich
   subsurface masses and layers. Downslope soil movements are more
   properly termed *solifluction, gelifluction* and *frost creep*, although many
   authors include the products of solifluction within the term cryoturbate.
   SYNONYMS: *cryoturbations* and (not recommended) congeliturbate.

cryoturbation (see also *cryoturbate; frost sorting*)
   [géliturbation]
1. (Singular) A collective term used to describe all soil movements due
   to *frost action.*
2. (Plural) Irregular structures formed in earth materials by deep *frost
   penetration* and *frost action* processes, and characterized by folded,
   broken and dislocated beds and lenses of unconsolidated deposits,
   included organic horizons and even bedrock.

   COMMENT: Cryoturbation encompasses *frost heave, thaw settlement*
   and all differential movements, including expansion and contraction
   due to temperature changes and the growth and disappearance of
   ground-ice bodies, whether perennial or seasonal. Low temperatures
   alone are not enough to produce cryoturbation; the water-ice phase
   change is necessary. Cryoturbation is an important process in the
   development of *patterned ground.*
   SYNONYMS: (not recommended) congeliturbation, frost churning,
   frost stirring.
   REFERENCES: French, 1976; Washburn, 1979.

crystocrene/chrystocrene (not recommended; see *icing*)

D

debris flow (see *mass wasting*)

degradation of permafrost (see *permafrost degradation*)

degree-day (see also *freezing index; thawing index*)
[degré-jour]
A measure of the departure of the mean temperature for a day from a given reference (or base) temperature.
> COMMENT: The *freezing index* and the *thawing index* are expressed in degree-days with respect to a reference temperature of 0°C (32°F); units: degree-day Celsius or degree-day Fahrenheit.
> REFERENCE: Boyd, 1979.

degree of saturation (of *frozen ground*)
[degré de saturation (du gélisol)]
1. The total degree of saturation of frozen soil is the ratio of the volume of ice and unfrozen water in the soil pores to the volume of the pores.
2. The degree of saturation by ice is the ratio of the volume of ice in the frozen soil pores to the volume of the pores.
> COMMENT: Neither definition is the equivalent of the standard definition used in soil mechanics where the degree of saturation is the ratio of the volume of water in a soil to the volume of the pores.

density of frozen ground
[densité du gélisol]
The mass of a unit volume of frozen soil or rock.

depressed-centre polygon (not recommended; see *polygon*)

depth of minimal annual amplitude (see *depth of zero annual amplitude*)

depth of thaw (see also *active layer*)
[profondeur de dégel]
The minimum distance between the ground surface and *frozen ground* at any time during the thawing season (see Figure 4).

depth of zero annual amplitude
[profondeur de l'amplitude annuelle nulle]
The distance from the ground surface downward to the level beneath which there is practically no annual fluctuation in ground temperature (see Figure 2).

> COMMENT: A change of no more than 0.1°C throughout the year is arbitrarily considered as practically no annual fluctuation. The temperature at the depth (or level) of zero annual amplitude ranges from about -0.1°C at the southern limit of the *permafrost region* to about -20°C in the extreme polar reaches of the zone of *continuous permafrost*. The depth of zero annual amplitude varies widely but generally lies between 10 and 20 m below the ground surface, depending on climatic and terrain conditions such as amplitude of annual surface temperature variation, vegetation, snow cover and characteristics of the soils and rocks including thermal diffusivity (see *thermal properties of frozen ground*).
> SYNONYMS: (not recommended) zone of minimum annual amplitude, zone of zero annual amplitude.
> REFERENCE: Muller, 1943.

depth to permafrost (see *permafrost table*)

detachment failure (see also *active-layer failure*)
[rupture par décollement]
A slope failure in which the thawed or thawing *active layer* and vegetation mat detach from the underlying frozen material (see Figure 21b).

> COMMENT: Detachment failures are common on colluvial slopes in areas of fine-grained, ice-rich deposits. They occur more frequently during warm summers or following disturbance of the vegetation or ground surface by, for example, tundra or forest fires or engineering activity, when the *depth of thaw* is greater than normal. Detachment failures that expose *massive ice* or icy sediments can develop into *retrogressive thaw slumps*.
> SYNONYMS: (not recommended) skin flow, active-layer glide.
> REFERENCES: Hughes, 1972; McRoberts and Morgenstern, 1974.

dielectric constant (see *electrical properties of frozen ground*)

diffusivity, thermal (see *thermal properties of frozen ground*)

dilation crack (see also *ice, dilation crack; thermal contraction crack*)
    [fissure de dilatation]
A tensile fracture in a frozen material due to surface extension caused by doming.
    COMMENT: This usually occurs during the growth of *frost mounds.*

discontinuous permafrost (see *permafrost, discontinuous*)

discontinuous permafrost zone (see *permafrost, discontinuous;* see also *permafrost zone*)

disequilibrium permafrost (see *permafrost, disequilibrium*)

drunken forest
    [forêt ivre]
Trees leaning in random directions in a permafrost region.
    COMMENT: A descriptive term for trees usually growing on ice-rich terrain and subject to repeated differential *frost heave* or *thermokarst* subsidence. Active, forested *rock glaciers* may also exhibit this phenomenon due to differential movements.
    REFERENCES: Muller, 1943; Zoltai, 1975.

dry density (see *density of frozen ground*)

dry frozen ground (see *frozen ground*)

dry permafrost (see *permafrost, dry*)

E

earth circle (not recommended; see *patterned ground*)

earth hummock (see *hummock, earth*)

earth mound (not recommended; see *frost mound;* see also *hummock, earth*)

East Greenland pingo (not recommended; see *pingo, open-system*)

electrical conductance (see *electrical properties of frozen ground*)

electrical properties of frozen ground

[propriétés électriques du gélisol]

The dielectric constant (or relative permittivity), electrical conductance and electrical resistivity are the major electrical properties governing the flow of electric current through frozen ground.

> COMMENT: The dielectric constant of a soil is a measure of the ability of the soil to store electrical energy in the presence of an electrostatic field; it is the ratio of the soil's permittivity to the permittivity of free space. The electrical conductance of a soil is the inverse of the resistance offered by a soil to current flow.

> Current flow under an electrical gradient in a frozen soil occurs almost entirely through the unfrozen water films. Electrical conduction is related to the thickness of these water films and their degree of interconnection; it decreases with decreasing temperature and increases with increasing pressure. As a consequence, all these electrical properties are influenced by soil type, density, salinity, temperature and, in particular, the *unfrozen water content*.

> For example, the resistivity of unfrozen soils increases slightly with decrease in temperature. A significant increase in resistivity occurs when the soil freezes, but this change is directly related to the *unfrozen water content* of the *frozen ground*. Available data show that the resistivities of frozen soils and rocks may be from 10 to more than 100 times larger than those of the same materials when unfrozen.

> Electromagnetic geophysical techniques for mapping permafrost, and the electrical grounding of various types of machines and electrical equipment, power transmission systems and radio transmitting antennae in permafrost areas, require a knowledge of the electrical properties of frozen ground.

> REFERENCE: Johnston, 1981.

electrical resistivity (see *electrical properties of frozen ground*)

epigenetic ice (see *ice, epigenetic*)

epigenetic ice wedge (see *ice wedge*)

epigenetic permafrost (see *permafrost, epigenetic*)

equilibrium permafrost (see *permafrost, equilibrium*)

excess ice (see *ice, excess*)

F

fabric (see *cryogenic fabric*)

felsenmeer (not recommended; see *block field*)

fen, string (see *string fen*)

fissure ice (see *ice, vein*)

fissure polygon (not recommended; see *polygon*)

flood ice (not recommended; see *icing*)

flood-plain icing (not recommended; see *icing*)

fluvio-thermal erosion (see *thermal erosion*)

foliated ice (see *ice, wedge*)

force, adfreezing (not recommended; see *strength, adfreeze*)

fossil ice wedge (not recommended; see *ice wedge*; see also *ice-wedge cast*)

fossil permafrost (not recommended; see *permafrost, relict*)

fossil pingo (not recommended; see *pingo scar*)

fossil thermokarst (not recommended; see *thermokarst*)

free water (see *water, pore*)

freezeback
[regel]
Refreezing of thawed materials.
> COMMENT: This term is used to describe:
> 1. seasonal refreezing of the thawed *active layer* (see Figure 4), or
> 2. refreezing of soil thawed as a result of construction activity or drilling of a well in permafrost, and of soil placed as backfill or a slurry around foundations or engineering facilities buried or embedded in frozen ground, e.g., pipelines, piles or shallow foundations in permafrost.
> REFERENCE: Johnston, 1981.

freeze-thaw action (see *frost action*)

freezing (of ground)
　　　　[engel (du sol)]
The changing of phase from water to ice in soil or rock.
　　　　COMMENT: The temperature at which ground freezing starts may be
　　　　lower than 0°C as a result of *freezing-point depression*.

freezing, artificial means (see *ground freezing, artificial*)

freezing, closed-system
　　　　[engel en système fermé]
Freezing that occurs under conditions that preclude the gain or loss of
any water in the system (see Figure 7).
　　　　COMMENT: Pure closed-system conditions, in which water is neither
　　　　added to nor removed from the system, are sometimes referred to as "in
　　　　situ freezing." Closed-system freezing of water-saturated soil causes
　　　　expansion equal to about 9% of the original pore volume of the
　　　　unfrozen soil.

freezing, in situ (see *freezing, closed-system*)

freezing, open-system
　　　　[engel en système ouvert]
Freezing that occurs under conditions that allow gain or loss of water in
the system by movement of *pore water* (see Figure 7).
　　　　COMMENT: The effects of open-system freezing can be quite different
　　　　for different soil materials. During freezing of clean, medium- to coarse-
　　　　grained materials, some *pore water* may be expelled ahead of the
　　　　freezing front (compensating for the volume increase during phase
　　　　change) thus reducing *frost heave*. During freezing of fine-grained
　　　　materials, however, water often migrates to the *freezing front*,
　　　　contributing to the formation of *segregated ice*, thus causing *frost
　　　　heave*.

freezing degree-day (see *degree-day*)

freezing front (see also *cryofront; thawing front*)
　　　　[front de gel]
The advancing boundary between *frozen* (or partially frozen) *ground* and
unfrozen ground (see figures 4 and 5).
　　　　COMMENT: In the usual case, where the *active layer* extends to the
　　　　permafrost table, two freezing fronts will be present during annual
　　　　freezing of the ground, one moving downward from the ground surface,
　　　　the other moving upward from the *permafrost table*.
　　　　　　The freezing front may not coincide with the 0°C isotherm
　　　　(*cryofront*).
　　　　SYNONYMS: (not recommended) freezing plane, frost front.
　　　　REFERENCES: Corte, 1962; Mackay, 1974a; van Everdingen, 1976.

freezing index (see also *degree-day; n-factor; thawing index*)

[indice de gel]

The cumulative number of *degree-days* below 0°C for a given time period.

> COMMENT: Four main types of air freezing indices have been used:
> 1. approximate freezing index – calculated from the mean monthly air temperatures for a specific station without making corrections for positive *degree-days* (above 0°C) in spring and fall (Boyd, 1973, 1979);
> 2. total annual freezing index – calculated by adding all the negative mean daily air temperatures (°C) for a specific station during a calendar year (Harris, 1981);
> 3. seasonal freezing index – calculated as the arithmetic sum of all the negative and positive mean daily air temperatures (°C) for a specific station during the time period between the highest point in the fall and the lowest point the next spring on the cumulative degree-day time curve (Huschke, 1959);
> 4. design freezing index – calculated by taking the average of the seasonal freezing indices for the three coldest winters in the most recent 30 years of record. If data for 30 years are not available, then the index is based on the coldest winter in the latest 10-year period of record (U.S. Army/Air Force, 1966).
>
> The total annual freezing index has been used to predict permafrost distribution, and the design freezing index is commonly used in engineering to estimate the maximum thickness of lake ice and the maximum depth of *frost penetration* in the ground.
>
> A surface (ground, pavement, etc.) freezing index differs from the air freezing index (see *n-factor*).

freezing plane (not recommended; see *freezing front*)

freezing-point depression (see also *ice-nucleation temperature*)

[abaissement du point de congélation]

The number of degrees by which the freezing point of an earth material is depressed below 0°C (see figures 2 and 3).

> COMMENT: The highest temperature at which soil, water, ice and air can coexist at equilibrium. In soils, the freezing-point depression is due mainly to capillarity and surface adsorption. It depends on soil particle effects (curvature and nature of soil particle surfaces), pressure, and the effects of dissolved solids in the *pore water*.
>
> The freezing-point depression can often be determined from the ground temperature profile where it is the difference between the temperature at the base of the *ice-bearing permafrost* and 0°C.
>
> REFERENCES; Anderson and Morgenstern, 1973; van Everdingen, 1976; Osterkamp and Payne, 1981.

freezing pressure
    [pression de gel]
The positive (heaving) pressure developed at ice-water interfaces in a soil
as it freezes.
>COMMENT: It is also known to result in a heaving pressure or frost-
>heave pressure that is responsible for the heaving of utilities,
>foundations and pavements. Ice-water interfaces occur at the contact of
>the *ice lenses* and the *frozen fringe*.
>REFERENCES: Jumikis, 1977; Andersland and Anderson, 1978;
>Johnston, 1981; Gilpin, 1982.

friable permafrost (see *permafrost, ice-bonded*)

frost (see *frozen ground; permafrost*)

frost, seasonal (see also *active layer*)
    [gel saisonnier]
The occurrence of ground temperatures below 0°C for only part of the
year.
>SYNONYMS: (not recommended) active frost, winter frost.

frost action (see also *frost heave; frost wedging*)
    [gélivation]
The process of alternate freezing and thawing of moisture in soil, rock
and other materials, and the resulting effects on materials and on
structures placed on, or in, the ground.
>COMMENT: Frost action in soils describes the detrimental processes
>of *frost heave* that occurs in the ground during the freezing period, and
>*thaw weakening* (followed by *thaw settlement*) that occurs as the
>*seasonally frozen ground* thaws.
>   Although it normally refers to seasonal freezing and thawing
>processes and effects, the term "frost action" has also been used to
>describe the long-term heaving that occurs when soils are subjected
>continuously to a freezing temperature over a long period of time
>(years), e.g., under cold storage plants and buried chilled pipelines.
>   Frost action contributes to the mechanical weathering
>(i.e., disintegration or breakdown) of soil and rock materials, by *frost
>wedging, cryoturbation* activity, and to the development of *cryotexture*
>and *cryogenic fabric* in soils.
>REFERENCES: Hennion, 1955; Washburn, 1979; Johnston, 1981.

frost blister (see also *icing blister; pingo, open-system*)
      [butte saisonnière à noyau de glace]
A seasonal *frost mound* produced through doming of *seasonally frozen ground* by a subsurface accumulation of water under high hydraulic potential during progressive *freezing* of the *active layer* (see figures 12 and 13).

> COMMENT: Freezing of the accumulated subsurface water produces a domed layer of clear ice beneath the overlying *frozen ground*. Frost blisters are formed in a single winter; their decay may take more than a year. They are distinguished from *icing blisters* by the layer of *seasonally frozen ground* overlying the ice layer.
> SYNONYMS: (not recommended) cryolaccolith, hydrolaccolith, seasonal pingo.
> REFERENCES: Muller, 1943; van Everdingen, 1978; Pollard and French, 1984.

frost boil (see also *patterned ground*)
      [ostiole]
A small mound of fresh soil material, formed by *frost action* (see Figure 16c, d).

> COMMENT: A type of nonsorted circle; they are commonly found in fine-grained sediments underlain by permafrost, but also occur in non-permafrost areas.
> SYNONYMS: mud boil, stony earth circle.
> REFERENCES: Thorn, 1976; Shilts, 1978.

frost bulb (see also *thaw bulb*)
      [bulbe de gel]
A more or less symmetrical zone of *frozen ground* formed around a buried chilled pipeline or beneath or around a structure maintained at temperatures below 0°C (see Figure 23).

> COMMENT: Heaving of the ground and/or of a structure or facility may occur as the frost bulb forms.
> REFERENCES: Andersland and Anderson, 1978; Johnston, 1981.

frost bursting (see *frost wedging*)

frost churning (not recommended; see *cryoturbation*)

frost circle (not recommended; see *patterned ground*)

frost crack (see *thermal contraction crack*)

frost-crack polygon (see *polygon*)

frost creep (see also *creep of frozen ground; frost action; gelifluction; solifluction*)
    [reptation due au gel]
The net downslope displacement that occurs when a soil, during a freeze-thaw cycle, expands normal to the ground surface and settles in a nearly vertical direction.
    REFERENCES: Benedict, 1970; Washburn, 1979.

frost fissure (see *thermal contraction crack*)

frost front (not recommended; see *freezing front*)

frost grip (see *adfreeze/adfreezing*)

frost heave (see also *frost action; ice, excess*)
    [soulèvement dû au gel]
The upward or outward movement of the ground surface (or objects on, or in, the ground) caused by the formation of ice in the soil (see Figure 7).

> COMMENT: *Frost action* in fine-grained soils increases the volume of the soil not only by freezing of in situ *pore water* ($\approx$ 9% expansion) but also by drawing water to the *freezing front* where *ice lenses* form. Soils that have undergone substantial heaving may consist of alternate layers of ice-saturated soil and relatively clear *ice lenses*. The lenses are formed normal to the direction of heat flow and when freezing penetrates from the ground surface (which may be horizontal, sloping or vertical), they form parallel to that surface. When unrestrained, the amount of surface heave may be almost as much as the total thickness of the *ice lenses*. Frost heave can occur seasonally or continuously if freezing of the ground proceeds without interruption over a period of years.
>
> Differential, or non-uniform, frost heaving is one of the main detrimental aspects of the *frost action* process and reflects the heterogeneous nature of most soils, or variations in heat removal rate and groundwater supply over short distances.
>
> Depending on the degree of restraint, large *freezing pressures* (up to 1 MPa) can be developed as the ground freezes. These can be transmitted to a foundation, structure or other object placed on the ground surface, or embedded or buried in the ground, as basal (i.e., vertical), forces acting on their underside, or through *adfreezing* of the soil to the sides of the foundation, structure or object.
> REFERENCES: Penner, 1967, 1968; Washburn, 1979; Linell and Lobacz, 1980; Chamberlain, 1981; Johnston, 1981.

frost-heave pressure (see *freezing pressure*)

frost hummock (not recommended; see *frost mound*)

frost jacking
[éjection gélivale]
Cumulative upward displacement of objects embedded in the ground, caused by *frost action.*

> COMMENT: Frost jacking results from basal or vertical *freezing pressures* acting on the underside of a foundation, structure or object, or from *adfreezing* of soil to the sides of these objects. The cumulative upward movement over a period of time (one or several freezing seasons) may result in the foundation unit or object being ejected from the ground.
>
> Fence posts and utility poles or towers are commonly affected, and both deep (pile) and shallow (post) foundations (e g., used for bridges, wharves, unheated or lightweight buildings) have been seriously affected by frost jacking.
>
> Blocks of jointed or fractured bedrock have also been displaced upward by frost jacking.
>
> SYNONYM: (not recommended) upfreezing.
> REFERENCE: Linell and Lobacz, 1980.

frost mound (see also *palsa; patterned ground*)
[butte cryogène]
Any mound-shaped landform produced by ground freezing combined with groundwater movement or the migration of soil moisture.

> COMMENT: Various types of frost mounds, (e.g., *frost blisters, icing blisters, palsas* and *pingos*) can be distinguished on the basis of their structure and duration, and the character of the ice contained in them.
> SYNONYMS: (not recommended) bugor, bulgunniakh, cryogenic mound, earth mound, frost hummock, ground-ice mound, tundra hummock.
> REFERENCES: Porsild, 1938; Muller, 1943; van Everdingen, 1978; Pollard and French, 1984.

frost penetration
[pénétration du gel]
The movement of the *freezing front* into the ground during freezing.

frost polygon (see *polygon*)

frost prying (see *frost wedging*)

frost riving (see *frost wedging*)

frost-sensitive soil (not recommended; see *frost-susceptible ground*)

frost shattering (see *frost wedging*)

frost sorting (see also *cryoturbation*)
[triage gélival]
The process of soil particle sorting by *frost action*.
REFERENCE: Washburn, 1979.

frost splitting (see *frost wedging*)

frost-stable ground (see also *frost-susceptible ground*)
[sol non gélif]
Ground (soil or rock) in which little or no *segregated ice* forms during
seasonal freezing.
COMMENT: Significant cumulative *ice segregation* and *frost heave*
may occur even in seasonally frost-stable ground (e.g., gravels and
rock) under conditions of continuous freezing and plentiful water
supply.
SYNONYM: (not recommended) non-frost-susceptible ground.
REFERENCES: van Everdingen, 1976; Chamberlain, 1981; Konrad
and Morgenstern, 1983.

frost stirring (not recommended; see *cryoturbation*)

frost suction (not recommended; see *cryosuction*)

frost-susceptible ground (see also *frost-stable ground*)
[sol gélif]
Ground (soil or rock) in which *segregated ice* will form (causing *frost
heave*) under the required conditions of moisture supply and temperature.
COMMENT: Frost-susceptible ground will eventually become *ice-rich*,
regardless of its initial *water content*, if the appropriate moisture supply
and temperature conditions persist. By implication, frost susceptible
ground may also be susceptible to *thaw weakening* effects when it
thaws.
SYNONYM: (not recommended) frost-sensitive soil.
REFERENCES: van Everdingen, 1976; Chamberlain, 1981; Konrad
and Morgenstern, 1983.

frost table (see *thawing front*)

frost weathering (see also *frost action; frost wedging*)
      [altération due au gel]
The disintegration and break-up of soil or rock by the combined action of *frost wedging* and hydration shattering.

> COMMENT: Hydration shattering is the process of grain loosening and soil or rock disintegration by the wedging pressure of water in films of varying thickness on the surfaces of silicate minerals. Water is drawn between the grains by various particle surface forces and exerts sufficient differential pressure to loosen and separate the grains. The process can act in all climates without the aid of freezing and thawing. When combined with freezing and thawing (*frost wedging*), however, the resulting process of frost weathering can be a very efficient mechanism for the break-up of soil or rock.
> SYNONYM: (not recommended) rock shattering.
> REFERENCES: White, 1976a; Washburn, 1979.

frost wedge (not recommended; see *thermal contraction crack*)

frost wedging (see also *frost action; frost weathering*)
      [gélifraction]
The mechanical disintegration, splitting or break-up of rock by the pressure of the freezing of water in cracks, crevices, pores, joints or bedding planes.

> COMMENT: A wide variety of terms has been used to describe what appears to be a single process.
> SYNONYMS: congelifraction, frost bursting, frost prying, frost riving, frost shattering, frost splitting, gelifraction.
> REFERENCE: Washburn, 1979.

frozen fringe
      [frange gelée]
The zone in a freezing, *frost-susceptible* soil between the warmest isotherm at which ice exists in pores and the isotherm at which the warmest *ice lens* is growing (see Figure 5).

> COMMENT: The temperature at the growing *ice lens* is slightly below 0°C.
> REFERENCES: Miller, 1972; Konrad and Morgenstern, 1983.

frozen ground (see also *cryostructure; cryotic ground; unfrozen ground*)
[gélisol]
Soil or rock in which part or all of the *pore water* consists of ice.

> COMMENT: Perennially and *seasonally frozen ground* can vary from being partially to extensively frozen depending on the extent of the phase change. It may be described as hard frozen, plastic frozen or dry frozen, depending on the *pore ice* and *unfrozen water contents* and its compressibility under load. Hard-frozen soils are firmly cemented by ice, are subject to brittle failure, and exhibit practically no consolidation under load. Plastic-frozen soils are cemented by ice but have viscous properties due to their high *unfrozen water content* and therefore will compress under load. Dry-, or friable-frozen, soils have a very low *total water content* and are not cemented by ice; their compressibility is the same as for unfrozen soils having the same composition, *water content* and density.
> REFERENCES: U.S.S.R., 1969, 1973; van Everdingen, 1976.

frozen ground creep (see *creep of frozen ground*)

frozen ground strength (see *mechanical properties of frozen ground*)

frozen zone (see *cryosphere*)

G

gas hydrate
[hydrate de gaz]
A special form of solid clathrate compound in which crystal lattice cages or chambers, consisting of host molecules, enclose guest molecules.

> COMMENT: Gas hydrates are formed under special temperature and pressure conditions. The host molecules are water, and the guest molecules may be a variety of gases, including argon, nitrogen, carbon dioxide, hydrogen sulfide, methane, ethane, halogens and other small molecules. In permafrost regions, gas hydrates are commonly found near the *permafrost base* and may lead to unexpected problems during drilling for hydrocarbons.
> REFERENCES: Bily and Dick, 1974; Kaplan, 1974; Judge, 1982.

gelifluction (see also *frost creep; solifluction*)
[gélifluxion]
The slow downslope flow of unfrozen earth materials on a frozen substrate.

> COMMENT: Gelifluction is a type of *solifluction* implying the presence of either *seasonal frost* or permafrost.
> REFERENCE: Washburn, 1979.

gelifraction (see *frost wedging*)

geocryology (see also *cryolithology; cryopedology; cryosol*)
[géocryologie]
The study of earth materials having a temperature below 0°C.
> COMMENT: The term is derived from the Russian word
> "geokriologiya." Although glaciers are not excluded, the term is usually
> applied to the study of *frozen ground*, including *seasonally frozen
> ground* as well as permafrost.
> REFERENCES: Fyodorov and Ivanov, 1974; Poppe and Brown, 1976;
> Washburn, 1979.

geothermal gradient (see *ground thermal regime*)

geothermal heat flux (see *ground thermal regime*)

glacier, rock (see *rock glacier*)

graveyard mound (not recommended; see *mound, thermokarst*)

ground, patterned (see *patterned ground*)

ground freezing, artificial
[congélation du sol]
The process of inducing or maintaining a frozen condition in earth
materials by artificial means.
> COMMENT: The frozen condition can be induced or maintained by
> natural convection movement of air, gases or liquids (e.g., through or in
> ventilation ducts, *thermal piles, thermosyphons*), or by forced
> (mechanical) circulation of cold air or a refrigerant through a system of
> ducts or freeze pipes in the ground.
> REFERENCES: Jumikis, 1977; Johnston, 1981.

ground freezing index (see *freezing index*)

ground heave (see *frost heave*)

ground ice (see *ice, ground*)

ground-ice mound (not recommended; see *frost mound*)

ground-ice slump (not recommended; see *retrogressive thaw slump*)

ground-ice wedge (not recommended; see *ice wedge*)

ground icing (not recommended; see *icing*)

ground settlement (see *thaw settlement*)

ground slumping (not recommended; see *thaw slumping;* see also *detachment failure; mass wasting*)

ground thawing index (see *thawing index*)

ground thermal regime
[régime thermique du sol]
A general term encompassing the temperature distribution and heat flows in the ground and their time-dependence (see Figure 2).

> COMMENT: Permafrost exists as a result of thermal conditions that maintain a ground temperature that does not rise above 0°C for at least two years. The ground temperature distribution is complicated, varying with depth from the surface and with time. Ground temperatures fluctuate in cyclical patterns on a daily and a yearly basis, in response to the heat losses and gains at the ground surface. The heat balance at the ground surface (which is indicated by the surface temperature) is highly variable with time, being affected by terrain and climate conditions as well by as the thermal properties of the ground itself.
>
> Changes in surface temperature impose a response that decays while travelling downwards. The rate of decay depends on the time scale involved, on the soil thermal properties and on the occurrence of freezing and thawing phenomena. The depth beyond which ground temperature fluctuations can be considered insignificant is the *depth of zero annual amplitude.* The effects of daily temperature variations at the ground surface penetrate to only a few centimetres; those due to weekly variations (e.g., transient weather systems) penetrate to perhaps several metres; and annual variations penetrate to a depth of about 10 to 20 metres. Longer-term changes in surface temperature caused by changes in climate and surface conditions may modify the ground thermal regime to much greater depths.
>
> Permafrost exists if the mean annual surface temperature is perennially below 0°C. Although the mean annual surface temperature may be below 0°C, the surface temperature will fluctuate during the year, causing a layer of ground immediately beneath the surface to thaw in the summer and freeze in the winter (the *active layer*). Small changes in the annual range of surface temperature and in the mean annual surface temperature from year to year, or over a period of a few years, may cause a layer of ground between the bottom of the *active layer* and the *permafrost table* to remain at a temperature above 0°C, creating a *talik* or *residual thaw layer.*
>
> The mean annual temperature of the ground usually increases with depth below the surface. In some northern areas, however, it is not uncommon to find that the mean annual ground temperature decreases

in the upper 50 to 100 metres below the ground surface as a result of past changes in surface and climate conditions. Below that depth, it will increase as a result of heat flow from the interior of the earth. The rate of change of temperature with depth in the earth is known as the geothermal gradient. The geothermal heat flux is the amount of heat escaping steadily from the earth by conduction through a unit area in unit time. It is generally calculated as the product of the geothermal gradient and the thermal conductivity of the earth materials at a given depth; its value is very small.

The geothermal gradient at a specific location can be determined from accurate measurements of ground temperature made at several depths to obtain the temperature profile over a period of time. A rough approximation of the mean annual surface temperature can be made by extrapolating the geothermal gradient to the ground surface. In permafrost areas, extrapolation of the gradient downwards to the point where the ground temperature changes from below to above 0°C will provide an estimate of the depth to the *permafrost base*. The ground thermal regime at various locations is often assessed using the mean annual ground temperature at the *depth of zero annual amplitude*. REFERENCES: Lachenbruch, 1959; Gold, 1967; Gold and Lachenbruch, 1973; Goodrich, 1982.

groundwater icing (not recommended; see *icing*)

H

hard frozen ground (see *frozen ground*)

heat, latent (see *thermal properties of frozen ground*)

heat capacity (see *thermal properties of frozen ground*)

heat pipe (see *thermosyphon*)

heave, basal (see *frost heave*)

heaving pressure (see *freezing pressure*; see also *frost heave*)

high-altitude permafrost (not recommended; see *permafrost, alpine*)

high-centre polygon (see *polygon*)

hummock, earth (see also *hummock, turf; thufur*)
     [butte de terre]
A hummock having a core of silty and clayey mineral soil and showing
evidence of *cryoturbation* (see Figure 20a, b).
> COMMENT: Earth hummocks are a type of nonsorted circle (see also
> *patterned ground*) commonly found in the zone of *continuous*
> *permafrost*. They develop in materials of a high silt and clay content
> and/or of high *ice content*. Earth hummocks found outside the southern
> limit of present-day permafrost are believed to have formed during a
> previous period of cooler climate when the area was underlain by
> permafrost.
> SYNONYMS: mud hummock and (not recommended) earth mound,
> tundra hummock.
> REFERENCES: Tarnocai and Zoltai, 1978; Washburn, 1979.

hummock, frost (not recommended; see *frost mound*)

hummock, mud (see *hummock, earth*; see also *patterned ground*)

hummock, peat (see *palsa*; see also *frost mound; thufur*)

hummock, tundra (not recommended; see *hummock, earth*)

hummock, turf (see also *hummock, earth; thufur*)
     [butte gazonnée]
A hummock consisting of vegetation and organic matter with or without
a core of mineral soil or stones (see Figure 20c).
> REFERENCES: Raup, 1966; Washburn, 1979.

hydration shattering (see *frost weathering*)

hydraulic pingo (see *pingo, open-system*)

hydraulic thawing
     [dégel hydraulique]
Artificial thawing and removal of *frozen ground* by the use of a stream or
jet of water under high pressure.
> COMMENT: Hydraulic thawing (hydraulicking) is a common method
> of working frozen placer deposits in North America.

hydrochemical talik (see *talik*)

hydrocryosphere (see *cryosphere*)

hydrofrost (not recommended; see *gas hydrate*)

hydrolaccolith (not recommended; see *frost blister; ice, intrusive; pingo*)

hydrostatic pingo (see *pingo, closed-system*)

hydrothermal talik (see *talik*)

I

ice
> [glace]

Frozen water; water in the solid state.
> COMMENT: In permafrost regions, ice may occupy voids in soils and rocks and may develop in a variety of forms. Ice may be colourless to pale blue or greenish-blue. It may appear white due to included gas bubbles; in exposures, ground ice may also appear black. Ice commonly occurs as hexagonal crystals. Various types of *ground ice* are defined below and elsewhere in this Glossary.

ice, aggradational (see also *permafrost aggradation*)
> [glace d'accroissement]

The additional, newly formed and newly incorporated *ground ice* resulting from aggradation of permafrost (see Figure 10a).
> COMMENT: *Ice lenses* form seasonally, especially in the lower part of the *active layer*, and can be incorporated into the permafrost if they do not melt over a period of years.
> REFERENCES: Mackay, 1972b, 1983; Cheng, 1983.

ice, buried (see also *ice, ground*)
> [glace enfouie]

Ice formed or deposited on the ground surface and later covered by sediments.
> COMMENT: Buried ice includes glacier, lake, river and sea ice, as well as *icings* and snow banks.

ice, cave
> [glace de caverne]

Naturally formed ice in a closed or open cave.
> COMMENT: Cave ice can form and persist in an area of temperate climatic conditions where the configuration of the cave or cave system permits an influx of cold winter air by gravity flow but limits access of warm summer air.
> REFERENCE: Harris, 1979.

ice, closed-cavity (see also *ice, open-cavity*)
  [glace de cavité fermée]
Ice formed in a closed space, cavity or cave in permafrost.

> COMMENT: Along the western Arctic coast of Canada, underground cavities, apparently formed by pockets of methane gas, have been found filled with ice crystals. The water from which the crystals have grown probably entered the cavity through vapour diffusion.
> REFERENCES: Mackay, 1965, 1972b.

ice, dilation crack (see also *dilation crack*)
  [glace de fissure de dilatation]
Ice that forms in *dilation cracks* (see Figure 10b).

> COMMENT: Dilation crack ice may form a significant component of the total *ice content* of features such as *pingos*. The ice is vertically banded and may be discoloured by inclusions of mineral soil and organic matter. Individual bands may be up to 20 cm wide.
> REFERENCES: Mackay, 1979, 1985.

ice, epigenetic (see also *ice, ground; ice, syngenetic*)
  [glace épigénétique]
Ground ice that formed some time after deposition of the earth material in which it occurs.

> COMMENT: If epigenetic ice occurs in the form of *ice lenses* in which the volume of ice to soil is large, the more descriptive term *segregated ice* is preferred. Examples of epigenetic ice also include *wedge ice* and *intrusive ice*.
> REFERENCE: Mackay, 1972b.

ice, excess (see also *frost heave; thaw settlement*)
  [glace en excès]
The volume of ice in the ground which exceeds the total pore volume that the ground would have under natural unfrozen conditions (see Figure 7).

> COMMENT: In standard soil engineering terminology, a soil is considered normally consolidated when its total pore volume or its *total water content* is in equilibrium with the acting gravity stresses. Due to the presence of *ground ice*, the *total water content* of a frozen soil may exceed that corresponding to its normally consolidated state when unfrozen. As a result, upon thawing, a soil containing excess ice will settle under its own weight until it attains its consolidated state.

ice, fissure (see *ice, vein*)

ice, foliated (see *ice, wedge*)

ice, fossil (not recommended; see *ice, relict*)

ice, ground (see also *ice, buried; ice, epigenetic; ice, intrusive; ice, syngenetic*)
> [glace de sol]

A general term referring to all types of ice formed in freezing and *frozen ground* (see Figure 10).
> COMMENT: Ground ice occurs in pores, cavities, voids or other openings in soil or rock and includes *massive ice*, but generally excludes *buried ice*. Ground ice may be epigenetic or syngenetic, contemporaneous or relict, aggrading or degrading, perennial or seasonal. It may occur as lenses, wedges, veins, sheets, seams, irregular masses, or as individual crystals or coatings on mineral or organic particles. Perennial ground ice can only occur within permafrost bodies.
> REFERENCES: Mackay, 1972b; Pollard and French, 1980.

ice, injection (not recommended; see *ice, intrusive*)

ice, interstitial (see *ice, pore*)

ice, intrusive (see also *ice, ground*)
> [glace intrusive]

Ice formed from water injected into soils or rocks (see Figure 10c).
> COMMENT: Freezing of injected water will normally lift the ground above it, thereby producing topographic forms somewhat resembling those of igneous intrusions in rocks. Thus, a tabular mass of intrusive ice is analogous to a sill or a dyke (see *ice, vein*) whereas the domed form is analogous to a laccolith (see *frost blister, pingo*). Use of terms such as "sill ice" or "hydrolaccolith," however, is not recommended. Intrusive ice may develop in porous unconsolidated sediments and in jointed or fractured bedrock. Fractures may become enlarged by hydraulic fracturing or *frost wedging* processes. For the greatest effect, water must become trapped in the joints or fractures and be subjected to relatively rapid freezing.
> SYNONYM: (not recommended) injection ice.
> REFERENCES: Mackay, 1972b; Dyke, 1981, 1984.

ice, lens (see also *ice, segregated; ice lens*)
> [glace de lentille]

Ground ice occurring as *ice lenses*.

ice, massive (see also *ice lens*)
　　　　[glace massive]
A comprehensive term used to describe large masses of *ground ice,*
including *ice wedges, pingo ice, buried ice* and large *ice lenses* (see
Figure 10d, e, f).

> COMMENT: Massive ice beds typically have an *ice content* of at least
> 250% (on an ice-to-dry-soil weight basis). If the *ice content* is less than
> 250%, the beds are better termed "massive icy beds." Some massive ice
> beds are more than 40 m thick and 2 km in horizontal extent, and
> some are responsible for prominent topographic rises.
> REFERENCES: Rampton and Mackay, 1971; Mackay, 1971, 1973a;
> Rampton and Walcott, 1974.

ice, needle
　　　　[aiguille de glace]
Long, thin, needle-like ice crystals that form perpendicular to the ground
surface (see Figure 10g).

> COMMENT: Needle ice forms during nights when there is extensive
> radiative cooling, causing *ice segregation* in the surface layer of the soil.
> The needles can form under stones, soil peds, moss or other surface
> vegetation and are best developed in alpine areas with maritime
> temperate climates where silty or organic soils are present. They can
> also form on coarse-grained, porous volcanic ejectamenta (e.g., in
> British Columbia and Iceland). The Swedish term "pipkrake" is
> sometimes used to describe needle ice.
> REFERENCES: Krumme, 1935; Mackay and Mathews, 1974;
> Washburn, 1979.

ice, open-cavity (see also *ice, closed-cavity*)
　　　　[glace de cavité ouverte]
Ice formed in an open cavity or crack in the ground by sublimation of
water vapour from the atmosphere.

> COMMENT: Open-cavity ice is similar to hoar frost, except that the
> ice crystals grow in cavities rather than on the surface. It is common in
> *thermal contraction cracks*, mine workings, ice caves and ice cellars in
> permafrost.
> SYNONYM: sublimation ice.
> REFERENCE: Mackay, 1972b.

ice, penecontemporaneous (not recommended; see *ice, syngenetic*)

ice, pingo (see also *pingo, closed-system; pingo, open-system*)
[glace de pingo]
Massive ice forming the core of a *pingo* (see Figure 10h).
> COMMENT: The ice in a pingo may be nearly pure or mixed with sediment. It includes *intrusive ice, segregated ice* and *dilation crack ice*.
> REFERENCES: Rampton and Mackay, 1971; Mackay, 1973b, 1985; Pissart and French, 1976.

ice, pore (see also *cryostructure; ice content; water, pore; water content, total; water content, unfrozen*)
[glace interstitielle]
Ice occurring in the pores of soils and rocks.
> COMMENT: Pore ice does not include *segregated ice*. On melting, pore ice does not yield water in excess of the pore volume of the same soil when unfrozen.
> SYNONYMS: ice cement, interstitial ice.
> REFERENCES: Brown and Kupsch, 1974; Johnston, 1981.

ice, relict (see also *permafrost, relict*)
[glace relictuelle]
Ice formed in, and remaining from, the geologically recent past.
> COMMENT: Relict ice may include *ground ice* preserved in cold regions such as the coastal plains of western Arctic Canada and northern Siberia, where permafrost of Pleistocene age has been preserved.
> SYNONYM: (not recommended) fossil ice.
> REFERENCES: Mackay et al., 1972; Mackay, 1975.

ice, reticulate
[glace réticulée]
A network of horizontal and vertical *ice veins* usually forming a three-dimensional, rectangular or square lattice (see Figure 9c, d).
> COMMENT: Field observations suggest that reticulate *ice veins* grow in horizontal and vertical shrinkage cracks with much of the water coming from the adjacent material in a semi-closed freezing system, rather than from migration of water in an open system. It is commonly found in frozen glaciolacustrine sediments.
> REFERENCE: Mackay, 1974b.

ice, segregated (see also *ice, lens; ice lens; ice segregation*)
[glace de ségrégation]
Ice formed by the migration of *pore water* to the *frozen fringe* where it forms into discrete layers or lenses (see Figure 9a).
> COMMENT: Segregated ice ranges in thickness from hairline to more than 10 m. It commonly occurs in alternating layers of ice and soil (see *ice lens*).
> SYNONYMS: (not recommended) ice gneiss, sirloin ice and Taber ice.
> REFERENCES: Taber, 1929; Mackay, 1966; Penner, 1972.

48

ice, sill (not recommended; see *ice, intrusive*)

ice, soil (not recommended; see *ice, ground*)

ice, sublimation (see *ice, open-cavity*)

ice, syngenetic (see also *ice, epigenetic; ice, ground*)
    [glace syngénétique]
Ground ice that formed more or less simultaneously with the deposition
of the earth material in which it occurs.
    SYNONYM: (not recommended) penecontemporaneous ice.

ice, thermal contraction crack (see also *ice, wedge; ice, vein*)
    [glace de fente de contraction thermique]
Ice formed in thermal contraction cracks in the ground (see Figure 17).
    COMMENT: Both *wedge ice* and some kinds of *vein ice* are types of
    thermal contraction crack ice. *Open-cavity ice* may be a constitutent of
    thermal contraction crack ice.
    REFERENCE: Mackay, 1972b.

ice, vein (see also *ice, thermal contraction crack; ice vein*)
    [glace de veine]
A comprehensive term for ice of any origin occupying cracks in
permafrost.
    COMMENT: Vein ice occurs in various forms, including horizontal
    layers or lenses, tabular sheets, wedges and reticulate nets.
    REFERENCES: Mackay, 1972b; Washburn, 1979.

ice, wedge (see also *ice, thermal contraction crack; ice wedge*)
    [glace de fente en coin]
Ice occurring in an *ice wedge* (see Figure 17).
    COMMENT: Wedge ice comprises a series of *ice veins* formed at the
    same location over a period of time. The ice is vertically to
    subvertically banded and may be discoloured by sediments and contain
    air bubbles that tend to be arranged in nearly vertical bands. The
    presence of many small bubbles may give the ice a milky appearance.
    Individual bands of ice are a few millimetres to a centimetre in width.
    REFERENCES: Gell, 1978; Washburn, 1979.

ice-bearing permafrost (see *permafrost, ice-bearing*)

ice blister (not recommended; see *icing blister*)

ice-bonded permafrost (see *permafrost, ice-bonded*)

ice cement (see *ice, pore*; see also *cryostructure; permafrost, ice bonded*)

ice content (see also *ice, pore; water content, total; water content, unfrozen*)
[teneur en glace]
The amount of ice contained in frozen or partially frozen soil or rock.
COMMENT: Ice content is normally expressed in one of two ways:
1. on a dry-weight basis (gravimetric), as the ratio of the mass of the ice in a sample to the mass of the dry sample, expressed as a percentage, or
2. on a volume basis (volumetric), as the ratio of the volume of ice in a sample to the volume of the whole sample, expressed as a fraction.

The volumetric ice content cannot exceed unity whereas the gravimetric ice content can greatly exceed 100%.
REFERENCES: Penner, 1970; Anderson and Morgenstern, 1973; Johnston, 1981.

ice-cored topography (see also *thermokarst terrain*)
[relief à noyaux de glace]
Topography that is due almost solely to differences in the amount of *excess ice* underlying its surface.
COMMENT: The relief may be totally or partially due to *thermokarst*, or to irregular development of *ground ice*, primarily *segregated ice*, or to buried glacier ice. An example is the "involuted hill" near Tuktoyaktuk, N.W.T.
REFERENCES: Rampton, 1974; Rampton and Walcott, 1974.

ice gneiss (not recommended; see *ice, segregated*)

ice lens (see also *ice, lens; ice, massive; ice, segregated*)
[lentille de glace]
A dominantly horizontal, lens-shaped body of ice of any dimension.
COMMENT: Ice lenses may range in thickness from hairline to more than 10 m. Very thick and extensive ice lenses are better termed *massive ice* beds. The term is commonly used for layers of *segregated ice* that are more or less parallel to the ground surface.
REFERENCES: Mackay, 1971, 1973a; Rampton and Walcott, 1974.

ice matrix (see *cryotexture*)

ice mound (not recommended; see *icing mound*)

ice-nucleation temperature (see also *freezing-point depression*)
    [température de nucléation de la glace]
The temperature at which ice first forms during freezing of a soil/water system that does not initially contain ice (see figures 2 and 3).

ice-rich permafrost (see *permafrost, ice-rich*)

ice segregation (see also *ice, segregated*)
    [ségrégation de la glace]
The formation of *segregated ice* in mineral or organic soils.
    COMMENT: The migration of *pore water* to the *freezing front* causes ice segregation.
    REFERENCES: Miller, 1972; Penner, 1972.

ice slump (not recommended; see *retrogressive thaw slump; thaw slumping*)

ice vein (see also *ice, vein*)
    [veine de glace]
An ice-filled crack or fissure in the ground.

ice wedge (see also *composite wedge; ice, wedge; sand wedge; soil wedge*)
    [coin de glace]
A massive, generally wedge-shaped body with its apex pointing downward, composed of foliated or vertically banded, commonly white, ice (see Figure 17).
    COMMENT: The size of ice wedges varies from less than 10 cm to more than 3 m in width at the top, commonly tapering to a feather edge at a depth of 1 to more than 10 m. Some ice wedges may extend downward as much as 25 m and may have shapes dissimilar to wedges. Epigenetic ice wedges are characteristically wedge-shaped, whereas syngenetic ice wedges are typically irregular in shape (see also *permafrost, epigenetic/syngenetic*).
    Ice wedges occur in *thermal contraction cracks* in which hoar frost (see *open-cavity ice*) forms and into which water from melting snow penetrates in the spring. Repeated annual contraction cracking of the ice in the wedge, followed by freezing of water in the crack, gradually increases the width and depth of the wedge and causes the vertical banding of the ice mass. The surface expression of ice wedges is generally a network of *polygons*. Ice wedges growing as a result of repeated (but not necessarily annual) winter cracking are called active ice wedges. They occur primarily in areas of *continuous permafrost* when developed in mineral soil. Inactive ice wedges can be stable and remain for many centuries without changing.
    REFERENCES: Dostovalov and Popov, 1966; Lachenbruch, 1966; Mackay and Black, 1973; French, 1976; Washburn, 1979; French et al., 1982; Mackay and Matthews, 1983.

ice wedge, fossil (not recommended; see *ice-wedge cast*)

ice-wedge cast (see also *composite wedge; sand wedge; soil wedge*)
[fente en coin fossile]
A filling of sediment in the space formerly occupied by an *ice wedge*.
> COMMENT: The term "fossil ice wedge" is not recommended because ice is no longer present. An ice-wedge cast is one of the few acceptable criteria indicating the earlier presence of permafrost.
> REFERENCES: Washburn, 1979, 1980.

ice-wedge polygon (see *polygon*)

ice-wedge pseudomorph (not recommended; see *ice-wedge cast*)

iciness (see also *ice content*)
[teneur en glace apparente]
A qualitative term describing the quantity of ice in *frozen ground*.
> COMMENT: In Russian literature, the equivalent term is used to describe the amount of ice contained in frozen, or partially frozen, soil or rock, expressed as the ratio of the mass of ice to the total mass of water (ice and unfrozen water) present.
> REFERENCE: U.S.S.R., 1969.

icing
[glaçage]
A sheetlike mass of layered ice formed on the ground surface, or on river or lake ice, by freezing of successive flows of water that may seep from the ground, flow from a spring or emerge from below river ice through fractures.
> COMMENT: Many icings incorporate snow. In North America the term "icing" is gradually replacing a variety of terms used in the past. Aufeis (German), flood ice, flood-plain icing, ice field, naled (Russian) and overflow ice usually indicated icings formed on river ice and floodplains. Chrystocrene (crystocrene), ground icing, groundwater icing and spring icing usually indicated icings formed by freezing of ground-water discharge. The term "taryn" is used in Siberia to indicate a thick icing that survives the summer. Use of the term "glacier" to describe icings, which is common in Alaska and Yukon, is inappropriate and should be discontinued. Icings also occur in non-permafrost areas.
> REFERENCES: Muller, 1943; Carey, 1970, 1973.

icing blister (see also *frost blister; icing mound*)
     [dôme de glaçage]
A seasonal *frost mound* consisting of ice only and formed at least in part
through lifting of one or more layers of an *icing* by injected water (see
figures 12 and 13).
> COMMENT: Freezing of the injected water will produce a layer of
> clear ice, contrasting with the overlying thinly layered ice of the icing.
> Rupture and draining of an icing blister may leave an empty cavity.
> Icing blisters are distinguished from *frost blisters* by the absence of a
> covering layer of *seasonally frozen ground*; they are distinguished from
> *icing mounds* by the layer of clear ice, and in some cases by the
> presence of an empty cavity. They have also been termed "ice blisters"
> (not recommended).
> REFERENCE: van Everdingen, 1978.

icing mound (see also *icing blister*)
     [butte de glaçage]
A seasonal *frost mound* consisting exclusively of thinly layered ice,
formed by freezing of successive flows of water issuing from the ground
or from below river ice (see Figure 13).
> COMMENT: Icing mounds may incorporate snow.
> SYNONYM: (not recommended) ice mound.
> REFERENCES: Muller, 1943; van Everdingen, 1978.

inactive ice wedge (see *ice wedge*)

inactive rock glacier (see *rock glacier*)

injection ice (see *ice, intrusive*)

in situ freezing (see *freezing, closed-system*)

interfacial water (see *water, pore*)

interstitial ice (see *ice, pore*)

intrapermafrost water (see also *subpermafrost water; suprapermafrost
water*)
     [eau d'intrapergélisol]
Water occurring in unfrozen zones (*taliks* and *cryopegs*) within
permafrost (see Figure 11).
> COMMENT: Intrapermafrost water includes water in open, lateral and
> transient *taliks* and in basal, isolated and marine *cryopegs*. Sometimes
> erroneously called interpermafrost water.
> REFERENCES: Williams, 1965, 1970; Tolstikhin and Tolstikhin, 1974.

intrusive ice (see *ice, intrusive*)

insular permafrost (not recommended; see *permafrost, discontinuous*)

island permafrost (not recommended; see *permafrost, discontinuous*)

isolated cryopeg (see *cryopeg*)

isolated talik (see *talik*)

L

lake talik (see *talik*)

latent heat (see *thermal properties of frozen ground*)

lateral talik (see *talik*)

level of zero annual amplitude (see *depth of zero annual amplitude*)

liquid water content (not recommended; see *water content, unfrozen*)

lobe, stone-banked/turf-banked (see *solifluction features*; see also *gelifluction*)

low-centre polygon (see *polygon*)

long-term strength (see *mechanical properties of frozen ground*)

M

Mackenzie Delta pingo (not recommended; see *pingo, closed-system*)

marine cryopeg (see *cryopeg*)

mass wasting
[mouvement de masse]
Downslope movement of soil or rock on, or near, the earth's surface under the influence of gravity (see Figure 21).

> COMMENT: Mass wasting includes slow displacements such as *frost creep, gelifluction* or *solifluction*, and more rapid movements such as earthflows or *active-layer failures*. It does not include crustal displacements resulting from tectonic activity or those movements where material is carried directly by an active transporting medium, such as glacial ice, snow, water or air. In permafrost areas, mass wasting is not limited to the *active layer*; it can include displacements caused by the formation and creep of *ground ice* within permafrost. When *frost heave* is a component of *frost creep*, it is a mass wasting process.
>
> REFERENCES: Hutchinson, 1968; Savage, 1968; Washburn, 1979.

massive ice (see *ice, massive*)

mechanical properties of frozen ground
[propriétés mécaniques du gélisol]
The properties of *frozen ground* governing its deformability and strength.

> COMMENT: 1. Properties under quasi-static loading:
>
> The behaviour of frozen soils under quasi-static loading is usually different from that of unfrozen soils because of the presence of ice and unfrozen water films. In particular, frozen soils are more susceptible to creep and relaxation effects, and their behaviour is strongly affected by temperature change. In addition to creep, volumetric consolidation may also develop in frozen soils with large *unfrozen water contents*.
>
> As with unfrozen soils, the strength of frozen soils depends on interparticle friction, particle interlocking and cohesion. In frozen soil, however, bonding of particles by ice is the dominant strength factor. This is complicated by the unfrozen water films surrounding the soil particles, which reduce interparticle bonding. The strength of ice in frozen soil is dependent on many factors, such as temperature, pressure, strain rate, grain size, crystal orientation and density. At very high *ice contents*, frozen soil behaviour under load is similar to that of ice. At low *ice contents*, however, when interparticle forces begin to contribute, the unfrozen water films play an important role, especially in fine-grained frozen soils.
>
> (a) Deformability and strength:
>
> The deformability and strength of a frozen soil can be studied by specially designed tests either in a cold room or in situ. Quasi-static elastic parameters usually determined in such tests are: Young's

modulus and Poisson's ratio for short-term response, and creep parameters (used in a creep equation) for long-term response. In addition, the variation of strength with time or with strain rate is also determined from the tests. The strength is usually found to vary from a high short-term value to a much smaller long-term value, which is considered to govern the behaviour of frozen soil under sustained loading. Under high confining stresses and at relatively high freezing temperatures, most frozen soils creep and eventually fail in a plastic manner. On the other hand, under compression at low confining stresses, or at tensile stresses combined with low temperatures, many frozen soils fail in a brittle manner by tensile crack propagation.

(b) Compressibility of frozen soils:

Although frozen soils are usually considered to be practically incompressible, and volume change deformations can therefore be neglected, investigations show, however, that the compressibility of frozen soils can be significant and should not be neglected in some cases, especially when large areas are loaded.

Compressibility and its time dependence in frozen soils are due to several causes, such as instantaneous compression of the gaseous phase, creep of the *pore ice* due to shear stresses at the grain contacts, and hydrodynamic consolidation due to the expulsion of unfrozen water under stress, the amount of which varies with the applied pressure.

2. Dynamic properties of frozen ground:

Information on the dynamic properties of frozen soils is important with regard to the behaviour of structures subjected to seismic or vibratory loads, and the evaluation of results of seismic field surveys in permafrost areas.

Dynamic properties are expressed either in terms of two dynamic elastic parameters: the dynamic modulus of elasticity and the dynamic Poisson's ratio, or in terms of the propagation velocities of compressional waves and shear waves in the material. The two sets of dynamic parameters are uniquely related by the theory of elasticity.

The dynamic elastic parameters deduced from wave propagation velocities are different from those obtained from any type of static loading tests because the latter contain the additional effects of elastic relaxation and creep. Parameters that influence the compressional and shear wave velocities in soils and rocks include grain size, lithology, *total water content*, porosity and pore structure, the nature, temperature and degree of freezing of the interstitial water, degree of cementation, and confining pressure.

Due to the *ice content*, seismic velocities are generally higher in frozen soils or rocks than in the same unfrozen materials. The change in velocity can occur gradually as temperatures decrease below °C, if *freezing point depression* conditions exist in the soil.

REFERENCES: Garg, 1973; Tsytovich, 1973; King et al., 1974; Vinson, 1978; Johnston, 1981.

mezhalasye (see *alas*)

moisture content (see *water content, total*; see also *ice content*)

mound, cemetery (not recommended; see *mound, thermokarst*)

mound, cryogenic (not recommended; see *frost mound*)

mound, graveyard (not recommended; see *mound, thermokarst*)

mound, peat (see *palsa*)

mound, permafrost (see *frost mound*)

mound, thermokarst (see also *thermokarst*)
      [butte de thermokarst]
A hummock remaining after melting of surrounding *ice wedges* in areas
of polygonal ground (see Figure 22e).
> COMMENT: Thermokarst mounds occur in groups forming a
> distinctive surficial network of regularly shaped mounds separated by
> troughs formed by the melting of *ice wedges*.
> SYNONYMS: (not recommended) baydzherakh, cemetery mound,
> graveyard mound.
> REFERENCES: Péwé, 1954; Brown, 1967a; French, 1975.

mud boil (see *patterned ground*; see also *frost boil*)

mud circle (see *patterned ground*)

mud-debris tongue (not recommended; see *solifuction features*)

mud hummock (see *hummock, earth*)

multiple retrogressive slide (see also *retrogressive thaw slump*)
      [glissement régressif multiple]
A type of mass movement associated with shear failure in unfrozen
sediments underlying permafrost, leading to detachment of blocks of
frozen ground that move downslope.
> COMMENT: A degree of back-tilting or rotation of the failure
> components may be involved.
> REFERENCE: McRoberts and Morgenstern, 1974.

N

naled (not recommended; see *icing*)

needle ice (see *ice, needle*)

net, nonsorted/sorted (see *patterned ground*)

n-factor (see also *freezing index; thawing index*)
[facteur n]
The ratio of the surface *freezing* or *thawing index* to the air *freezing* or *thawing index*.

COMMENT: At any site, (standard) air temperatures are seldom the same as surface (air/substrate) temperatures. Because air temperatures (measured at weather stations) are usually available and surface temperatures are not, the n-factor (an empirically determined coefficient) is used to relate air temperatures to surface temperatures in order to establish the thermal boundary condition at the surface, particularly for engineering purposes.

The difference between air and surface temperatures at any specific time and location is greatly influenced by climatic, surface and subsurface conditions (e.g., latitude, cloud cover, time of day or year, wind speed, type of surface – wet, dry, moss, snow, natural vegetated terrain, mineral soil, pavements – and ground thermal properties). The average surface temperature and n-factor can change significantly from year to year, even for a given surface and location, as well as for different sites, surfaces and soil systems.

Values of the freezing and thawing n-factors have been determined for a large number of sites and surfaces and are widely used for predicting surface temperatures and the *ground thermal regime*. The data vary widely, however, and indicate that a rigorous value of n for a given site cannot simply be chosen from these data. Direct determination of the n-factor for a specific location is much better and requires concurrent observations of air and surface temperatures throughout at least one and preferably several complete freezing and thawing seasons.

REFERENCES: Carlson and Kersten, 1953; Lunardini, 1978, 1981.

noncryotic (see *noncryotic ground*)

noncryotic ground (see also *cryotic ground; thawed ground; unfrozen ground*)
[sol non cryotique]
Soil or rock at temperatures above 0°C (see figures 2 and 3).

COMMENT: Noncryotic ground is not synonymous with *thawed ground* (which implies an earlier frozen state), nor with *unfrozen ground* (the temperature of which may be below 0°C).
REFERENCE: van Everdingen, 1976.

non-frost-susceptible ground (not recommended; see *frost-stable ground*;
see also *frost-susceptible ground*)

nonsorted circle/net/polygon/step/stripe (see *patterned ground*)

O

offshore permafrost (see *permafrost, subsea*)

open-cavity ice (see *ice, open-cavity*)

open-system freezing (see *freezing, open-system*)

open-system pingo (see *pingo, open-system*)

open talik (see *talik*)

organic cryosol (see *cryosol*)

organic terrain (not recommended; see *peatland*)

oriented lake (see also *thermokarst; thermokarst lake*)
    [lac orienté]

One of a group of *thermokarst lakes* possessing a common, preferred,
long-axis orientation (see Figure 22b).
    COMMENT: Oriented lakes appear to develop by differential erosion
of permafrost shorelines formed in fine-grained, homogeneous
sediments under the influence of predominant winds. In some cases,
bedrock structural control may also determine lake orientation.
Oriented lakes also occur in non-permafrost environments.
    REFERENCES: Black and Barksdale, 1949; Rex, 1961; Carson and
Hussey, 1962; Price, 1968; Sellmann et al., 1975; Harry and French,
1983.

overflow ice (not recommended; see *icing*)

P

palsa (see also *frost mound; peat plateau*)
    [palse]
A peaty permafrost mound possessing a core of alternating layers of *segregated ice* and peat or mineral soil material (see figures 14 and 15a).
    COMMENT: Palsas are typically between 1 and 7 m in height and less than 100 m in diameter. The term is of Fennoscandian origin, originally meaning "…a hummock rising out of a bog with a core of ice" (Seppälä, 1972). Implicit in this definition are their constructional nature, their origin in wetlands (fens or peat bogs), and that *ice segregation* in mineral soil beneath peat is the process responsible for growth. Most, but not all, palsas occur in the zone of *discontinuous permafrost*.
    A more general definition has been proposed by Washburn (1983) in which the term is applied in a descriptive sense to a broader range of permafrost mounds that may include *intrusive* as well as *segregated ice*: "Palsas are peaty permafrost mounds, ranging from about 0.5 to about 10 m in height and exceeding about 2 m in average diameter, comprising (1) aggradation forms due to *permafrost aggradation* at an *active-layer/*permafrost contact zone, and (2) similar-appearing degradation forms due to disintegration of an extensive peaty deposit." The disadvantage of this broader definition is that mounds of entirely different origins (e.g., those including *intrusive ice*) are grouped under one term. It is proposed, therefore, that the term "palsa" be restricted to those features where the internal structure shows the presence of *segregated ice* and where the environment lacks high hydraulic potentials, provided that other parameters (size, shape, location in wetlands) are also satisfied. The term *"frost mound"* should be used as a non-genetic term to describe the range of morphologically similar, but genetically different, features that occur in permafrost terrain.
    SYNONYMS: peat hummock; peat mound.
    REFERENCES: Lundqvist, 1969; Seppälä, 1972; Zoltai and Tarnocai, 1971, 1975; Washburn, 1983.

palsa plateau (not recommended; see *peat plateau*)

partially-bonded permafrost (see *permafrost, ice-bonded*)

passive method of construction (see *construction methods in permafrost*)

patterned ground (see also *frost boil; frost mound; polygon; solifluction features; thufur*)

[sol structuré]

A general term for any ground surface exhibiting a discernibly ordered, more-or-less symmetrical, morphological pattern of ground and, where present, vegetation (see Figure 16).

> COMMENT: Patterned ground is not confined to *permafrost regions* but is best developed in regions of present or past intensive *frost action*. A descriptive classification of patterned ground includes such features as nonsorted and sorted circles, nets, *polygons*, steps and stripes, and *solifluction features*. In *permafrost regions*, the most ubiquitous macro-form is the *ice-wedge polygon*, and a common micro-form is the nonsorted circle. The latter includes mud boils, mud hummocks, *frost boils*, stony earth circles, *earth hummocks, turf hummocks, thufa* and (not recommended) tundra hummocks. Nonsorted circles are not all of the same origin. Some, such as mud and *earth hummocks* and *frost boils*, involve *cryoturbation* activity and differential heave of *frost-susceptible* materials. Others, such as mud boils, involve hydraulic pressures and diapiric displacements of water-saturated sediments. The genesis of many types of patterned ground phenomena is not clearly understood.
>
> Patterned ground also occurs in *peatland* in the form of *string fens* and other peatland features not listed in this Glossary (see Stanek, 1977 and Stanek and Worley, 1983).
>
> REFERENCES: Washburn, 1956, 1979; Mackay and MacKay, 1976; Tarnocai and Zoltai, 1978; Shilts, 1978; Mackay, 1980.

peat (see *peatland*)

peatland

[tourbière]

Peat-covered terrain.

> COMMENT: Stanek (1977) and Stanek and Worley (1983) should be consulted for definitions and information on peat and peatland and associated features.
>
> There is no international agreement on the minimum thickness of peat required for the terrain to be classified as "peatland." In Canada, peatland is defined as a type of wetland formed by the accumulation of plant remains with negligible decomposition.
>
> In the zone of *discontinuous permafrost*, especially near the southern limit, peatland is often underlain by permafrost, reflecting the thermal insulating qualities of peat. *Palsas, peat plateaus* and *polygonal peat plateaus* are permafrost-related peatland features (see Figure 15).
>
> SYNONYMS: (not recommended) muskeg; organic terrain.
>
> REFERENCES: Zoltai and Tarnocai, 1975; Stanek, 1977; Tarnocai, 1980; Stanek and Worley, 1983.

peat hummock (see *palsa*; see also *frost mound; thufur*)

peat mound (see *palsa*)

peat plateau (see also *palsa; polygonal peat plateau*)
[plateau palsique]
A generally flat-topped expanse of peat, elevated above the general
surface of a *peatland*, and containing *segregated ice* that may or may not
extend downward into the underlying mineral soil (see figures 14
and 15b).
> COMMENT: Some controversy exists as to whether peat plateaus and
> *palsas* are morphological variations of the same features, or genetically
> different. Layers or lenses of *segregated ice* occur especially in the
> mineral soil but they are thinner and less extensive in peat plateaus than
> in *palsas*. Flat-topped, somewhat raised *peatlands* without an icy core
> occur in non-permafrost environments but are not peat plateaus.
> SYNONYM: (not recommended) palsa plateau.
> REFERENCES: Brown, 1970a; Zoltai, 1972; Zoltai and Tarnocai,
> 1975.

penetrating talik (not recommended; see *talik*)

pereletok (not recommended; see *permafrost*; see also *residual thaw
layer*)
[pérélétok]
A layer of ground, between the *active layer* above and the permafrost
below, that remains frozen for one or several years and then thaws.
> COMMENT: Use of this Russian term is not recommended. It
> presupposes arbitrarily that pereletok is not permafrost although the
> definition assigns a sufficient duration of time for it to be considered as
> permafrost. Furthermore, the definition implies a basic difference in
> characteristics between pereletok, on the one hand, and permafrost of
> only a few years' duration, on the other hand, where in fact no
> difference exists. It is preferable to regard *frozen ground* as permafrost
> if it lasts at least from one winter through the succeeding thawing
> season to the next winter, and as *seasonally frozen ground* if it lasts
> only through part of a year. For the same reason, the use of the term
> "climafrost" as a synonym for pereletok is not recommended.
> REFERENCE: Brown, 1966.

perennially cryotic ground (see *cryotic ground*; see also *permafrost*)

perennially frozen ground (see *permafrost*)

perforating talik (not recommended; see *talik*)

pergelic soil (not recommended; see *cryosol*)

periglacial

[périglaciare]

The conditions, processes and landforms associated with cold, nonglacial environments.

> COMMENT: The term was originally used to describe the climatic and geomorphic conditions of areas peripheral to Pleistocene ice sheets and glaciers. Modern usage refers, however, to a wider range of cold climatic conditions regardless of their proximity to a glacier, either in space or time. Many, but not all, periglacial environments possess permafrost; all are dominated by *frost action* processes.
>
> REFERENCES: Dylik, 1964; French, 1976; Washburn, 1979.

permacrete

[géliciment]

An artificial mixture of frozen soil materials cemented by *pore ice*, which forms a concrete-like construction material used in cold regions.

> COMMENT: When soils of appropriate gradation are brought to their saturation moisture content, mixed and compacted to maximum density and then frozen, a material of relatively high strength is obtained so long as it is kept frozen. Permacrete has been moulded in brick or block form or placed in forms and used for construction (e.g., of walls and columns, both underground in tunnels, mines, etc., and on the ground surface in a freezing environment).
>
> REFERENCE: Swinzow, 1966.

permafrost

[pergélisol]

Ground (soil or rock) that remains at or below 0°C for at least two years (see Figure 2).

> COMMENT: Permafrost is synonymous with perennially *cryotic ground*: it is defined on the basis of temperature. It is not necessarily frozen, because the freezing point of the included water may be depressed several degrees below 0°C; moisture in the form of water or ice may or may not be present. In other words, whereas all perennially frozen ground is permafrost, not all permafrost is perennially frozen. Permafrost should not be regarded as permanent, because natural or man-made changes in the climate or terrain may cause the temperature of the ground to rise above 0°C. Permafrost includes perennial *ground ice*, but not glaciers or bodies of surface water with temperatures perennially below 0°C. The thickness of permafrost may range from less than 1 m to more than 1000 m. Russian usage requires the continuous existence of temperatures below 0°C for at least three years. (See *pereletok*, not recommended)
>
> SYNONYMS: perennially frozen ground, perennially cryotic ground and (not recommended) biennially frozen ground, climafrost, cryic layer, permanently frozen ground.
>
> REFERENCES: Muller, 1943; van Everdingen, 1976; Kudryavtsev, 1978.

permafrost, acoustically-defined (see *permafrost, ice-bonded*; see also *permafrost, subsea*)

permafrost, alpine
[pergélisol alpin]
Permafrost existing at high altitudes in middle and low latitudes (see Figure 1).

> COMMENT: Alpine permafrost grades into the permafrost of high latitudes in areas such as the North American Cordillera. Plateau permafrost is a subdivision of alpine permafrost but use of this term is not recommended.
> REFERENCES: Fujii and Higuchi, 1978; Harris and Brown, 1978, 1982; Péwé, 1983.

permafrost, contemporary (see *permafrost, equilibrium*)

permafrost, continuous (see also *permafrost, alpine; permafrost, discontinuous; permafrost boundary*)
[pergélisol continu]
Permafrost occurring everywhere beneath the exposed land surface throughout a geographic region with the exception of widely scattered sites, such as newly deposited unconsolidated sediments, where the climate has just begun to influence the *ground thermal regime* causing the formation of continuous permafrost (see Figure 1).

> COMMENT: For practical purposes, the existence of small *taliks* within the zone of continuous permafrost has to be recognized.
> REFERENCE: Brown, 1970b.

permafrost, discontinuous (see also *permafrost, alpine; permafrost, continuous; permafrost boundary*)
[pergélisol discontinu]
Permafrost occurring in some areas beneath the exposed land surface throughout a geographic region where other areas are free of permafrost (see Figure 1).

> COMMENT: The zone of discontinuous permafrost lies between the zone of *continuous permafrost* and the southern limit of permafrost in lowlands. Near its northern boundary, discontinuous permafrost is widespread, whereas near its southern boundary it occurs in isolated patches or islands and is commonly referred to as "sporadic" permafrost. There is no sharp distinction, or boundary, between the zones of *continuous* and *discontinuous permafrost*.
> SYNONYMS: (not recommended) insular permafrost; island permafrost; scattered permafrost.
> REFERENCE: Brown, 1970b.

permafrost, disequilibrium (see also *permafrost, equilibrium;*
permafrost, relict; permafrost, subsea)
    [pergélisol en déséquilibre]
Permafrost that is not in thermal equilibrium with the existing mean
annual ground-surface or sea-bottom temperature and the geothermal
heat flux.
    REFERENCE: Mackay, 1972a.

permafrost, dry (see also *permafrost, thaw-stable*)
    [pergélisol sec]
Permafrost containing neither free water nor ice.
    COMMENT: A negligible quantity of moisture in the form of
    interfacial water may be present (see *water, pore*). Dry permafrost is
    thaw-stable.
    REFERENCE: van Everdingen, 1976.

permafrost, epigenetic (see also *permafrost, syngenetic*)
    [pergélisol épigénétique]
Permafrost that formed after the deposition of the soil material in which
it occurs.

permafrost, equilibrium (see also *permafrost, disequilibrium;*
permafrost, relict; permafrost, subsea)
    [pergélisol en équilibre]
Permafrost that is in thermal equilibrium with the existing mean annual
ground-surface or sea-bottom temperature and with the geothermal heat
flux.
    SYNONYM: contemporary permafrost.
    REFERENCE: Mackay, 1972a.

permafrost, high-altitude (not recommended; see *permafrost, alpine*)

permafrost, ice-bearing (see also *permafrost, ice-bonded*)
    [pergélisol contenant de la glace]
Permafrost that contains ice.

permafrost, ice-bonded (see also *cryostructure*)
  [pergélisol cimenté par la glace]
Ice-bearing permafrost in which the soil particles are cemented together
by ice.

> COMMENT: Soils may be partially-bonded, poorly-bonded or friable
> if the soil particles are held together (cemented) weakly by the ice. If
> ice bonding is strong, the soil is said to be well-bonded. The distinction
> between ice-bonded permafrost and permafrost that contains ice but in
> which the ice does not act as a cement, is particularly important in
> *subsea permafrost*, where the salinity of the *pore water* affects the
> ability of ice to act as a cement. Acoustic geophysical methods can be
> used to delineate *ice-bonded permafrost*, but use of the term
> "acoustically-defined permafrost" is not recommended except as a
> modifier to describe the method used to determine the permafrost
> conditions.
> REFERENCES: Pihlainen and Johnston, 1963; Linell and Kaplar,
> 1966; Johnston, 1981; Hunter, 1984; Sellmann and Hopkins, 1984.

permafrost, ice-rich (see also *permafrost, thaw-sensitive*)
  [pergélisol à haute teneur en glace]
Permafrost containing *excess ice.*

> COMMENT: A qualitative term. Ice-rich permafrost is *thaw-sensitive.*

permafrost, island (not recommended; see *permafrost, discontinuous)*

permafrost, planetary
  [pergélisol cosmique]
Permafrost occurring on other planetary bodies (planets, moons,
asteroids).

> COMMENT: The most extensive suite of permafrost-related features
> known is from Mars, where large volumes of water and/or ice are
> believed to exist beneath the planet's surface. Water ice, alone or in
> combination with methane ice and/or *gas hydrates*, is also believed to
> occur on moons of Jupiter (Callisto, Ganymede and Europa) and
> Saturn (Titan). Most of the moons and asteroids of the solar system are
> characterized by permafrost (temperature perennially below 0°C), but
> in the absence of any water they are all unfrozen, although *cryotic.* All
> the planetary bodies noted above include some frozen material.
> REFERENCES: Anderson et al., 1973; Fanale and Clark, 1983.

permafrost, relict (see also *ice, relict; permafrost, disequilibrium; permafrost, equilibrium*)

[pergélisol relictuel]

Permafrost reflecting past climatic conditions differing from those of today.

> COMMENT: Relict permafrost formed when the ground surface temperature was different (usually lower) than at present, and its temperature is now in disequilibrium with the present mean annual ground surface temperature. This permafrost persists in places where it could not form today.
> SYNONYM: (not recommended) fossil permafrost.
> REFERENCE: Mackay et al., 1972.

permafrost, saline (see also *cryopeg*)

[pergélisol salin]

Permafrost in which part or all of the water content is unfrozen because of *freezing-point depression* due to salinity of the *pore water*.

> COMMENT: Saline permafrost is found in *cryopegs*. At temperatures below the *ice-nucleation temperature*, a higher than normal *unfrozen water content* will persist due to increased salinity of the remaining *pore water*.

permafrost, sea-bed/sea-bottom (not recommended; see *permafrost, subsea*)

permafrost, seasonally-active (see also *active layer*)

[pergélisol saisonnièrement actif]

The uppermost layer of the permafrost which undergoes seasonal phase change due to the *freezing-point depression* of its *pore water* (see figures 2 and 4).

> REFERENCE: van Everdingen, 1985.

permafrost, sporadic (see *permafrost, discontinuous*)

permafrost, submarine (not recommended; see *permafrost, subsea*)

permafrost, subsea (see also *permafrost, disequilibrium; permafrost, equilibrium; permafrost, ice-bearing; permafrost, ice-bonded*)
[pergélisol sous-marin]
Permafrost occurring beneath the sea bottom (see figures 1 and 11).

> COMMENT: Subsea permafrost either occurs in response to negative sea-bottom water temperatures, or it formed in now submerged coastal areas that were exposed previously to air temperatures below O°C (*relict permafrost*).
>
> Much of the *ice-bonded permafrost* that has been found beneath the sea bottom has been inferred from acoustic geophysical surveys, and the term "acoustically-defined permafrost" has been used to describe such permafrost found in areas where temperature records or visual confirmation of ice bonding are not available.
> SYNONYMS: (not recommended) sea-bed permafrost, submarine permafrost, sub-seabed permafrost.
> REFERENCES: Mackay, 1972a; Hunter et al., 1976.

permafrost, syngenetic (see also *permafrost, epigenetic*)
[pergélisol syngénétique]
Permafrost that formed more or less simultaneously with the deposition of the soil material in which it occurs.

permafrost, thaw-sensitive (see also *permafrost, ice-rich; permafrost, thaw-stable*)
[pergélisol sensible au dégel]
Perennially frozen ground which, upon thawing, will experience significant *thaw settlement* and suffer loss of strength to a value significantly lower than that for similar material in an unfrozen condition.

> COMMENT: *Ice-rich permafrost* is thaw-sensitive.
> SYNONYM: (not recommended) thaw-unstable permafrost.
> REFERENCES: Linell and Kaplar, 1966; van Everdingen, 1976.

permafrost, thaw-stable (see also *permafrost, dry; permafrost, thaw-sensitive*)
[pergélisol stable au dégel]
Perennially *frozen ground* which, upon thawing, will not experience either significant *thaw settlement* or loss of strength.

> COMMENT: Thaw-stable permafrost may have the same mineral and particle-size compositions as *thaw-sensitive permafrost*. It may be *frost-susceptible*. *Dry permafrost* is thaw-stable.
> REFERENCE: Linell and Kaplar, 1966.

permafrost, thaw-unstable (not recommended; see *permafrost, thaw-sensitive*)

permafrost, widespread (see *permafrost, discontinuous*)

permafrost aggradation (see also *ice, aggradational; permafrost degradation*)
> [accroissement du pergélisol]

A naturally or artificially caused increase in the thickness and/or areal extent of permafrost.

> COMMENT: Permafrost aggradation may be caused by climatic cooling and changes in terrain conditions, including vegetation succession, infilling of lake basins and a decrease in snow cover. It can also occur under ice arenas, road and airfield embankments, etc. It may be expressed as a thinning of the *active layer* and a thickening of the permafrost, as well as an increase in the areal extent of permafrost.

permafrost base (see also *permafrost table*)
> [base du pergélisol]

The lower boundary surface of permafrost, above which temperatures are perennially below 0°C (cryotic) and below which temperatures are perennially above 0°C (noncryotic) (see figures 2 and 4).

permafrost boundary (see also *permafrost, continuous; permafrost discontinuous; permafrost limit*)
> [limite du pergélisol]

1. The margin of a discrete body of permafrost.
2. The geographical boundaries between the zones of *continuous* and *discontinuous permafrost*.

permafrost creep (see *creep of frozen ground*)

permafrost degradation (see also *permafrost aggradation*)
> [régression du pergélisol]

A naturally or artificially caused decrease in the thickness and/or areal extent of permafrost.

> COMMENT: Permafrost degradation may be caused by climatic warming or by changes in terrain conditions, such as disturbance or removal of an insulating vegetation layer by fire, or by flooding caused by a landslide-blocked stream, or by human activity. It may be expressed as a thickening of the *active layer,* a lowering of the *permafrost table*, a raising of the *permafrost base*, or a reduction in the areal extent or the complete disappearance of permafrost.

permafrost island (see *permafrost, discontinuous*)

permafrost limit (see also *permafrost boundary; permafrost zone*)
> [frontière du pergélisol]

Outermost (latitudinal) or lowest (altitudinal) limit of the occurrence of permafrost (see Figure 1).

permafrost mound (see *frost mound*)

permafrost region (see also *cryosphere; permafrost zone*)
[région pergélisolée]
A region in which the temperature of some or all of the ground remains continuously at or below 0°C for at least two years.

> COMMENT: The permafrost region is commonly divided into *permafrost zones* (see Figure 1).

permafrost table (see also *permafrost base*)
[plafond du pergélisol]
The upper boundary of permafrost (see figures 2 and 4).

> COMMENT: The depth of this boundary below the land surface, whether exposed or covered by a water body or glacier ice, is variable depending on such local factors as topography, exposure to the sun, insulating cover of vegetation and snow, drainage, grain size and degree of sorting of the soil, and thermal properties of soil and rock.
> REFERENCES: Muller, 1943; Stearns, 1966; Washburn, 1979.

permafrost thickness
[épaisseur du pergélisol]
The vertical distance between the *permafrost table* and the *permafrost base* (see figures 2 and 4).

permafrost zone (see also *permafrost, continuous; permafrost, discontinuous; permafrost limit; permafrost region*)
[zone de pergélisol]
A major division of a *permafrost region* (see Figure 1).

> COMMENT: A *permafrost region* is commonly divided into zones based on the proportion of the ground that is perennially *cryotic*. The basic division in high latitudes is into zones of *continuous permafrost* and *discontinuous permafrost*.
> REFERENCES: Muller, 1943; Brown, 1967b, 1978; Washburn, 1979; Péwé, 1983.

permanently frozen ground (not recommended; see *permafrost*)

permittivity, relative (see *electrical properties of frozen ground*)

piercing talik (not recommended; see *talik*)

pingo

[pingo]

A perennial *frost mound* consisting of a core of *massive ice*, produced primarily by injection of water, and covered with soil and vegetation.

> COMMENT: Pingos occur in the zones of *continuous* and *discontinuous permafrost.* The term "pingo," a local Inuktitut term used in the Mackenzie Delta, Canada, was applied to relatively large features with heights of 10 m or more and horizontal dimensions of more than 100 m. Most pingos are conical, somewhat asymmetric, and have a circular or oval base and a fissured top that may be cratered. The fissures and craters are the result of rupturing of the soil and vegetation cover during doming due to progressive development of the ice core (see *dilation crack*). Seasonal *frost mounds* (e.g., *frost blisters*), should not be called pingos.
>
> SYNONYMS: (not recommended) bulgunniakh, hydrolaccolith.
>
> REFERENCES: Porsild, 1938; Mackay, 1973b, 1979; Washburn, 1979.

pingo, closed-system (see also *ice, pingo*)

[pingo en système fermé]

A *pingo* formed by doming of frozen ground due to freezing of injected water supplied by expulsion of *pore water* during *aggradation of permafrost* in the closed *talik* under a former water body (see figures 18 and 19a).

> COMMENT: Most closed-system pingos are found in flat, poorly-drained terrain in the zone of *continuous permafrost.* Repeated injections of expelled water into the overlying permafrost, followed by freezing of the injected water, cause progressive doming, and produce the *massive ice* forming the core of the pingo. Progressive formation of *segregated ice* and *dilation crack ice* can also contribute to the process.
>
> SYNONYMS: hydrostatic pingo and (not recommended) Mackenzie Delta pingo.
>
> REFERENCES: Mackay, 1973b, 1979, 1985.

pingo, hydraulic (see *pingo, open-system*)

pingo, open-system (see also *frost blister; ice, pingo*)

    [pingo en système ouvert]

A pingo formed by doming of frozen ground due to freezing of injected water supplied by groundwater moving downslope through *taliks* to the site of the pingo, where it moves towards the surface (see Figure 19b).

    COMMENT: Most open-system pingos are found in or near areas of marked relief, mainly in the zone of *discontinuous permafrost*. High hydraulic potential, due to water originating in elevated areas, causes repeated injection of water into the weakest portion of the permafrost, followed by freezing. This leads to the development of the *massive ice* forming the core of the pingo.

    SYNONYMS: hydraulic pingo and (not recommended) East Greenland pingo.

    REFERENCES: Müller, 1959; Hughes, 1969.

pingo, seasonal (not recommended; see *frost blister; frost mound*)

pingo ice (see *ice, pingo*)

pingo remnant (see also *pingo; pingo scar*)

    [pingo effondré]

A collapsed pingo (see Figure 19c).

    COMMENTS: In contemporary permafrost environments, a pingo remnant is commonly represented by a low, circular or arcuate ridge of material resulting from the slumping of the sides of the pingo during thawing. The former centre is marked by a depression which may be filled with water.

    REFERENCES: Black, 1969; Washburn, 1979.

pingo scar (see also *pingo; pingo remnant*)

    [pingo fossile]

A *pingo remnant* in a contemporary, non-permafrost environment.

    COMMENT: Their occurrence provides evidence of former permafrost conditions.

    SYNONYM: (not recommended) fossil pingo.

    REFERENCE: Flemal, 1976.

pipkrake (see *ice, needle*)

pit, thermokarst (see *thermokarst terrain*)

planetary permafrost (see *permafrost, planetary*)

plastic frozen ground (see *frozen ground*)

plateau permafrost (not recommended; see *permafrost, alpine*)

polygon (see also *patterned ground*)
   [polygone]
A type of *patterned ground* consisting of a closed, roughly equidimensional figure bounded by more or less straight sides; some of the sides may be irregular (see Figure 16a, b).

> COMMENT: Macro-scale polygons, typically 15 to 30 m across, result from thermal contraction cracking of the ground and form random or oriented polygonal patterns. They occur in both mineral terrain and *peatland* (see *polygonal peat plateau*). Ice-wedge polygons are common in poorly drained areas and may be either high-centred or low-centred. Sand-wedge polygons occur where wedges of primary mineral infill underly the polygon boundaries. Some polygons may be formed by seasonal frost cracking in areas of deep *seasonal frost*.
> Micro-scale polygonal patterns, usually less than 2 m in diameter, are normally caused by desiccation cracking.
> SYNONYMS: frost polygon, frost-crack polygon, and (not recommended) depressed-centre polygon, fissure polygon, raised-centre polygon, Taimyr polygon, tundra polygon
> REFERENCES: Rapp and Clark, 1971; Washburn, 1979.

polygon, tundra (not recommended; see *polygon*)

polygonal ground (see *patterned ground*)

polygonal peat plateau (see also *peat plateau*)
   [plateau palsique à polygones]
A *peat plateau* with ice-wedge polygons (see Figure 15c).

> COMMENT: Polygonal peat plateaus are commonly found near the boundary between the zones of *discontinuous* and *continuous* *permafrost*.
> REFERENCES: Zoltai and Tarnocai, 1975; Zoltai and Pollett, 1983.

poorly-bonded permafrost (see *permafrost, ice-bonded*)

pore ice (see *ice, pore*)

pore water (see *water, pore*)

pressure, freezing-induced (see *freezing pressure*; see also *frost jacking*)

pressure-melting
[fonte sous pression]
Lowering the melting point of ice by applying pressure.

> COMMENT: Application of pressure increases the *unfrozen water content* by a small amount in frozen soils at a given temperature. Ice in soils is more easily melted by this process than bulk ice, because of stress concentrations at the soil intergranular contacts.
> REFERENCES: Anderson and Morgenstern, 1973; Glen, 1974.

R

raised-centre polygon (not recommended; see *polygon*)

relict permafrost (see *permafrost, relict*)

relict active layer (see *active layer, relict*)

residual stress (see also *thaw consolidation*)
[contrainte résiduclle]
The effective stress generated in a thawing soil if no volume change is permitted during thaw.

> REFERENCES: Morgenstern and Nixon, 1971; Nixon and Morgenstern, 1973.

residual thaw layer (see also *active layer; talik*)
[couche dégelée résiduelle]
A layer of *thawed ground* between the *seasonally frozen ground* and the *permafrost table* (see Figure 4).

> COMMENT: This layer may result from thawing of the permafrost which causes a lowering of the *permafrost table*, or from incomplete freezing of the *active layer* during a mild winter after a very warm summer, or during a winter in which an unusually heavy snowfall (providing a thick insulating cover on the ground surface) occurs before extreme cold sets in. It may exist for one year or for several years, or it may be permanent if permafrost is degrading due to climatic warming or changes in terrain conditions resulting from natural or human disturbance or activity. This layer does not exist where the *seasonal frost* extends to the *permafrost table*.
> REFERENCE: Linell and Kaplar, 1966.

resistivity, electrical (see *electrical properties of frozen ground*)

retrogressive-thaw flow slide (not recommended; see *retrogressive thaw slump*)

retrogressive thaw slump (see also *active-layer failure; multiple retrogressive slide; thaw slumping*)

[glissement régressif dû au dégel]

A slope failure resulting from thawing of *ice-rich permafrost* (see Figure 21c, d).

> COMMENT: Retrogressive thaw slumps consist of a steep headwall that retreats in a retrogressive fashion due to thawing, and a debris flow formed by the mixture of thawed sediment and meltwater that slides down the face of the headwall and flows away. Such slumps are common in ice-rich glaciolacustrine sediments and fine-grained diamictons.
>
> SYNONYMS: (not recommended) bi-modal flow, ground-ice slump, ice slump, retrogressive-thaw flow slide, thermocirque, thermo-erosional cirque.
>
> REFERENCES: Mackay, 1966; Rampton and Mackay, 1971; Hughes, 1972; McRoberts and Morgenstern, 1974; Washburn, 1979.

ribbed fen (see *string fen*)

river talik (see *talik*)

rock blister (not recommended; see *frost action*)

rock glacier

[glacier rocheux]

Found on slopes, a mass of rock fragments and finer material that contains either interstitial ice or an ice core and shows evidence of past or present movement.

> COMMENT: Rock glaciers do not form where there is insufficient moisture to form the interstitial ice that permits movement of the mass. Some are believed to have been formed, at least partly, by burial of glacier ice. Active rock glaciers move at speeds up to 50 m per year and possess steep fronts with slope angles greater than the angle of repose. Rock glaciers are said to be inactive when the main body ceases to move. Most rock glaciers have transverse ridges and furrows on their surface.
>
> REFERENCES: Capps, 1910; White, 1976b; Washburn, 1979.

rock shattering (not recommended; see *frost weathering*)

S

saline permafrost (see *permafrost, saline*)

salinity (see *water, pore*)

sand wedge (see also *composite wedge; ice wedge; ice-wedge cast; soil wedge; thermal contraction crack*)
[coin de sable]
A wedge-shaped body of sand produced by filling of a *thermal contraction crack* with sand either blown in from above or washed down the walls of the crack (see Figure 17h).
> COMMENT: A sand wedge may be considered as a wedge of primary filling; it is not a replacement feature associated with the melting of an ice *wedge*. It is a type of *soil wedge* showing marked vertical fabric and laminations.
> SYNONYM: (not recommended) tesselation.
> REFERENCES: Berg and Black, 1966; Black, 1976; Washburn, 1979; Mackay and Matthews, 1983.

sand-wedge polygon (see *polygon*)

saturation, degree of (see *degree of saturation*)

scattered permafrost (not recommended; see *permafrost, discontinuous*)

sea-bed permafrost (not recommended; see *permafrost, subsea*)

seasonal frost (see *frost, seasonal*)

seasonal pingo (not recommended; see *frost blister; frost mound*)

seasonally frozen ground (see also *active layer*)
[gélisol saisonnier]
Ground that freezes annually (see figures 2 and 4).
> COMMENT: In areas with permafrost, seasonally frozen ground can include the uppermost portion of the permafrost (see *seasonally thawed ground*).

seasonally thawed ground (see also *active layer*)
[sol saisonnièrement dégelé]
Ground that thaws annually (see figures 2 and 4).
> COMMENT: In areas with permafrost, seasonally thawed ground can include the uppermost portion of the permafrost in places where annual thawing takes place at temperatures below 0°C, as a result of *freezing-point depression* due to saline *pore water* or a high clay content.

segregated ice (see *ice, segregated*)

segregation potential
[potentiel de ségrégation]
The ratio of the rate of moisture migration to the temperature gradient in
a frozen soil near the 0°C isotherm.

> COMMENT: An engineering parameter that couples mass (water) flow
> and heat flow in a freezing soil. It is used by some workers to predict
> amounts of *frost heave*.
> REFERENCES: Nixon, 1982; Konrad and Morgenstern, 1983, 1984.

short-term strength (see *mechanical properties of frozen ground*)

sirloin ice (not recommended; see *ice, segregated*)

skin flow (not recommended; see *active-layer failure; detachment failure*)

soil, frost-sensitive (not recommended; see *frost-susceptible ground*)

soil, frost-stable (see *frost-stable ground*)

soil, frost-susceptible (see *frost-susceptible ground*)

soil, frozen (see *frozen ground*)

soil, non-frost-susceptible (not recommended; see *frost-stable ground*)

soil wedge (see also *composite wedge; ice wedge; ice-wedge cast; sand
wedge; thermal contraction crack*) ⁻
[coin de sol]
A wedge-shaped body of soil that is different in structure and texture
from the surrounding soil (see Figure 17g).

> COMMENT: A soil wedge may be an *ice-wedge cast* (i.e., a feature of
> secondary filling), or a *sand wedge* (i.e., a feature of primary filling), or
> it may be produced by repeated frost cracking of *seasonally frozen
> ground* followed by filling of the crack with soil. It is usually difficult to
> distinguish between soil wedges in the *active layer*, soil occupying
> cracks in *seasonally frozen ground* (i.e., in a non-permafrost
> environment), soil as original fillings in cracks in permafrost, and soil
> replacing *ice wedges*.
> REFERENCES: Jahn, 1975; Black, 1976; Washburn, 1979.

soliflual garland terrace (not recommended; see *solifluction features*)

solifluction (see also *frost creep; gelifluction*)
    [solifluxion]
Slow downslope flow of saturated unfrozen earth materials (see Figure 16d).

    COMMENT: The presence of a frozen substrate, or even freezing and thawing is not implied in the original definition (Andersson, 1906). However, one component of solifluction can be the *creep of frozen ground*. Rates of flow vary widely. The term is commonly applied to processes operating in both *seasonal frost* and permafrost areas.
    REFERENCES: Andersson, 1906; Washburn, 1979.

solifluction features (see also *patterned ground*)
    [formes dues à la solifluxion]
Physiographic features (see Figure 16d) of varying scale produced by the process of *solifluction*.

    COMMENT: Typical solifluction features include:
1. apron – a fan-like deposit at the base of a slope;
2. lobe – an isolated, tongue-shaped feature, up to 25 m wide and 150 m or more long, formed by more rapid *solifluction* on certain sections of a slope showing variations in gradient; commonly has a steep (15°-60°) front and a relatively smooth upper surface. Fronts covered by a vegetation mat are called "turf-banked lobes" whereas those that are stony are called "stone-banked lobes."

    SYNONYM: (not recommended) mud-debris tongue.
3. sheet – a broad deposit of nonsorted, water-saturated, locally derived materials that is moving or has moved downslope. Stripes are commonly associated with solifluction sheets.

    SYNONYM: solifluction mantle.
4. terrace – a low step, or bench, with a straight or lobate front, the latter reflecting local differences in rate of flow. A solifluction terrace may have bare mineral soil on the upslope part and 'folded under' organic matter in both the seasonally thawed and the frozen soil. Those covered with a vegetation mat are called "turf-banked terraces"; those that are stony are called "stone-banked terraces."

    SYNONYMS: solifluction bench, solifluction step and (not recommended) soliflual garland terrace.
    REFERENCES: Brown, 1969; Benedict, 1970; Washburn, 1979.

sorted circle/net/polygon/step/stripe (see *patterned ground*)

southern limit of permafrost (see *permafrost limit*)

sporadic permafrost (see *permafrost, discontinuous*)

spring icing (not recommended; see *icing*)

static cryosol (see *cryosol*)

step, nonsorted/sorted (see *patterned ground*)

stone-banked lobe/terrace (see *solifluction features*; see also *gelifluction*)

stone field (see *block field*)

stone net (see *patterned ground*)

stony earth circle (see *patterned ground*)

strength, adfreeze (see also *adfreeze/adfreezing*)
      [résistence de la congélation adhérente]
The tensile or shear stress required to separate two objects that are
bonded together by ice.
      COMMENT: The term is usually used to describe the resistance to the
      force that is required to separate *frozen ground* or an ice mass from an
      object (frequently a foundation unit) to which it is frozen. The shear
      stress required to separate an object from *frozen ground* is frequently
      referred to as the "tangential adfreeze strength."
      REFERENCES: Muller, 1943; Johnston, 1981.

strength, creep/delayed/long-term/short-term (see *mechanical properties
of frozen ground*)

strength, tangential adfreeze (see *strength, adfreeze*)

stress, residual (see *residual stress*; see also *thaw consolidation*)

string bog (see *string fen*)

string fen
      [tourbière réticulée]
A *peatland* with roughly parallel narrow ridges of peat dominated by
fenland vegetation interspersed with slight depressions, many of which
contain shallow pools (see Figure 15d).
      COMMENT: The ridges or strings are arranged at right angles to the
      slope, which is usually less than 2°. They are typically 1 to 3 m wide,
      up to 1 m high and may be over 1 km long. Although the ridges are
      usually parallel to one another, they may interconnect at acute angles.
      On nearly level fens the ridges are farther apart but shorter, and they
      interconnect frequently, giving a roughly polygonal appearance. Since
      the strings are elevated, they are better drained and allow shrubs and
      trees to grow on them. String fens are composed of sedge-fen peat with
      some woody shrub remains. The ridges are composed of moss-sedge or
      moss peat. They are best developed in the zone of *discontinuous*

permafrost and immediately to the south of the *permafrost region*. In the central and northern parts of the zone of *discontinuous permafrost*, the ridges are often perennially frozen. Permafrost conditions may extend into the underlying soil.

SYNONYMS: string bog, ribbed fen.

REFERENCES: Zoltai, 1971; Zoltai and Tarnocai, 1975; Tarnocai, 1980; Zoltai and Pollett, 1983.

stripe, nonsorted/sorted (see *patterned ground*)

sublimation ice (see *ice, open-cavity*)

submarine permafrost (not recommended; see *permafrost, subsea*)

subpermafrost water (see also *intrapermafrost water; suprapermafrost water*)

[eau de subpergélisol]

Water occurring in the *noncryotic ground* below the permafrost (see Figure 11).

COMMENT: This term does not include the water in basal *cryopegs*, i.e., the unfrozen zones that may occur in the basal portion of the permafrost (see *intrapermafrost water*).

REFERENCES: Williams, 1965, 1970; Tolstikhin and Tolstikhin, 1974.

subsea permafrost (see *permafrost, subsea*)

sub-seabed permafrost (not recommended; see *permafrost, subsea*)

subsurface ice (not recommended; see *ice, ground*)

suprapermafrost water (see also *active layer; intrapermafrost water; subpermafrost water*)

[eau de suprapergélisol]

Water occurring in unfrozen zones (*taliks*) above perennially *frozen ground* (see Figure 11).

COMMENT: Suprapermafrost water occurs in the *active layer*, between the *active layer* and the *permafrost table*, and in *taliks* below rivers and lakes. It is replenished by infiltration of rain, snowmelt or surface waters, or from *intra-* or *subpermafrost water* via open *taliks*. Much of the suprapermafrost water in the *active layer* may freeze in the winter; the remainder can temporarily become confined and subjected to increasing pressure during progressive freezing of the *active layer* (see *cryogenic aquiclude*).

REFERENCES: Williams, 1965, 1970; Tolstikhin and Tolstikhin, 1974.

surface freezing/thawing index (see *freezing index; thawing index;* see also *n-factor*)

syngenetic ice (see *ice, syngenetic*)

syngenetic ice wedge (see *ice wedge*)

syngenetic permafrost (see *permafrost, syngenetic*)

T

Taber ice (not recommended; see *ice, segregated*)

talik (see also *cryopeg; residual thaw layer; thaw basin*)
    [talik]
A layer or body of *unfrozen ground* in a permafrost area (see Figure 11).
    COMMENT: Taliks may have temperatures above 0°C (noncryotic) or below 0°C (cryotic, forming part of the permafrost). Several types of taliks can be distinguished on the basis of their relationship to the permafrost (closed, open, lateral, isolated and transient taliks), and on the basis of the mechanism responsible for their unfrozen condition (hydrochemical, hydrothermal and thermal taliks):

1. closed talik – a noncryotic talik occupying a depression in the *permafrost table* below a lake or river (also called "lake talik" and "river talik"); its temperature remains above 0°C because of the heat storage effect of the surface water;
2. hydrochemical talik – a cryotic talik in which freezing is prevented by mineralized groundwater flowing through the talik.
3. hydrothermal talik – a noncryotic talik, the temperature of which is maintained above 0°C by the heat supplied by groundwater flowing through the talik;
4. isolated talik – a talik entirely surrounded by perennially *frozen ground*; usually cryotic (see isolated *cryopeg*), but may be noncryotic (see transient talik);
5. lateral talik – a talik overlain and underlain by perennially frozen ground; can be noncryotic or cryotic;
6. open talik – a talik that penetrates the permafrost completely, connecting *suprapermafrost* and *subpermafrost water*, (e.g., below large rivers and lakes). It may be noncryotic (see hydrothermal talik) or cryotic (see hydrochemical talik).

SYNONYMS: (not recommended) through talik, penetrating talik, perforating talik, piercing talik;

7. thermal talik – a noncryotic talik, the temperature of which is above 0°C due to the general thermal regime. It includes the *seasonally thawed ground* in the *active layer*;
8. transient talik – a talik that is gradually being eliminated by freezing, e.g., the initially noncryotic closed talik below a small lake which, upon draining of the lake, is turned into a transient isolated talik by *permafrost aggradation* (see also *pingo, closed-system*).

REFERENCES: Williams, 1965; Washburn, 1973; van Everdingen, 1976.

Taimyr polygon (not recommended; see *polygon*)

tangential adfreeze strength (see *strength, adfreeze*)

taryn (see *icing*)

temperature profile (see *ground thermal regime*)

terrace, stone-banked/turf-banked (see *solifluction features*; see also *gelifluction*)

tesselation (not recommended; see *sand wedge*)

thaw basin (see also *talik; thaw bulb; thaw sink; thermokarst lake*)
[cuvette de dégel]
A depression of the *permafrost table* created by naturally induced thawing.

COMMENT: In *permafrost regions*, thaw basins exist beneath bodies of water such as lakes or rivers that do not freeze to the bottom in winter. They may be quite extensive both in depth (from a few metres to more than a 100 m) and in areal extent (from several tens of metres to more than 2 km) and they may be irregular in shape. Their depth, areal extent and shape depend on the size of the water body, the type and properties of earth material underlying it, and the presence of *ground ice* and groundwater.

SYNONYM: closed talik and (not recommended) thaw depression.

thaw bulb (see also *frost bulb; thaw basin*)
    [bulbe de dégel]
A more or less symmetrical area of thaw in permafrost surrounding a man-made structure (see Figure 23).

    COMMENT: Construction and operation of structures usually lead to alteration of the *ground thermal regime*. Where permitted, the development of a thaw bulb under a structure is taken into account and controlled as part of the engineering design. It is frequently nearly symmetrical in form and limited in size under structures such as buildings. Beneath linear structures or facilities built in permafrost areas, such as road embankments or buried warm pipelines, the thaw bulb may extend for the full length of the structure. Settlement of the ground and the structure or facility may occur as the thaw bulb forms.

    A thaw bulb may also form when a structure or facility, around which a *frost bulb* has developed, is abandoned and the ground is no longer maintained at a temperature below 0°C.

    REFERENCES: Andersland and Anderson, 1978; Johnston, 1981.

thaw consolidation (see also *residual stress; thaw consolidation ratio; thaw settlement*)
    [consolidation due au dégel]
Time-dependent compression resulting from thawing of *frozen ground* and subsequent drainage of *pore water*.

    COMMENT: If during thaw, the flow of water from the thawed soil is unimpeded, then the variation of settlement with time is controlled solely by the position of the *thawing front*. If the thawed soil is not sufficiently permeable, and flow is impeded, however, the rate of settlement with time is also controlled by the compressibility and permeability of the *thawed ground*.

    In the case of thawing fine-grained soils, if the rate of thaw is sufficiently fast, water is released at a rate exceeding that at which it can flow from the soil, and pore pressures in excess of hydrostatic will be generated. These excess pore pressures may cause severe instability problems in slopes and foundation soils.

    It has been found that excess pore pressures and the degree of consolidation in thawing soils depend principally on the *thaw consolidation ratio*.

    REFERENCES: Morgenstern and Nixon, 1971; Andersland and Anderson, 1978; Johnston, 1981.

thaw consolidation ratio (see also *thaw consolidation; thaw settlement*)
  [coefficient de consolidation au dégel]
A dimensionless ratio of the rate of thaw to the rate of consolidation of
the thawing soil, which is considered to be a measure of the relative rates
of generation and expulsion of excess pore fluids during thaw.

  COMMENT: According to Morgenstern and Nixon (1971), a value of
  the ratio greater than unity would predict the danger of sustained
  substantial pore pressures at the *thawing front* and hence the possibility
  of instability due to the reduction of shear strength at that plane.
  REFERENCES: Morgenstern and Nixon, 1971; Johnston, 1981.

thaw depression (not recommended; see *thaw basin*)

thaw excavation (see *construction methods in permafrost*)

thaw hole (not recommended; see *thaw sink*)

thaw lake (not recommended; see *thermokarst; thermokarst lake*)

thaw pit (not recommended; see *thaw sink*)

thaw-sensitive permafrost (see *permafrost, thaw-sensitive*; see also
permafrost, thaw-stable)

thaw settlement (see also *ice, excess; thaw consolidation; thaw
consolidation ratio; thaw strain*)
  [tassement dû au dégel]
Compression of the ground due to *thaw consolidation* (see Figure 7).

  COMMENT: In coarse-grained and dense soils, the amount of thaw
  settlement is small because it is governed mainly by the melting of the
  pore ice. In ice-rich soils, however, the amount of thaw settlement may
  be quite substantial.
    In general, on thawing, any *frozen ground* will settle both under
  its own weight and under applied stresses. The settlement will continue
  as long as the *thawing front* advances and until the pore pressures
  generated during thawing are dissipated.
    In relatively permeable coarse-grained soils, where drainage of
  pore water is rapid, the thaw settlement rate will usually follow closely
  the rate of thaw, and development of pore pressures will be negligible
  during the thaw period. On the other hand, if a relatively impermeable
  fine-grained soil is thawed rapidly, then excess pore pressures will be
  generated. If these excess pore pressures are sustained for any length of
  time, then severe problems may develop (e.g., slopes may become
  unstable, dam foundations may fail, and differential settlements may be
  aggravated).
  REFERENCES: Andersland and Anderson, 1978; Johnston, 1981.

thaw sink (see also *thermokarst*)
      [doline de dégel]
A closed *thaw basin* with subterranean drainage.
      SYNONYMS: (not recommended) thaw hole, thaw pit.
      REFERENCES: Wallace, 1948; Hopkins, 1949.

thaw slumping (see also *detachment failure*)
      [glissement dû au dégel]
A slope failure mechanism characterized by the melting of *ground ice*,
and downslope sliding and flowing of the resulting debris.
      COMMENT: The resulting landform is a *retrogressive thaw slump*.
      SYNONYM: (not recommended) ice slump.
      REFERENCES: Mackay, 1966; McRoberts and Morgenstern, 1974;
      Washburn, 1979.

thaw softening (see *thaw weakening*)

thaw-stable permafrost (see *permafrost, thaw-stable*)

thaw strain (see also *thaw consolidation; thaw settlement*)
      [déformation due au dégel]
The amount that *frozen ground* compresses upon thawing.
      COMMENT: The thaw strain is equal to the *thaw settlement* divided
      by the original thickness of the *frozen ground* that thawed. When
      freezing of the ground occurred in a closed system, the thaw strain is
      due only to the 9% volume contraction associated with the melting
      of ice.

thaw-unstable permafrost (not recommended; see *permafrost, thaw
sensitive*)

thaw unconformity (see *active layer, relict*)

thaw weakening (see also *frost action*)
      [affaiblissement dû au dégel]
The reduction in shear strength due to the decrease in effective stresses
resulting from the generation and slow dissipation of excess pore
pressures when frozen soils containing ice are thawing.
      COMMENT: Thaw weakening, although generally used with respect to
      the thawing of *seasonally frozen ground* when melting of *ice lenses* and
      pore ice occurs, is equally applicable to thawing of perennially frozen
      soils. The usual effects of thaw weakening are a significant decrease in
      bearing capacity and an increase in stability problems (e.g., on road
      embankments, natural slopes, etc.)
      SYNONYM: thaw softening.
      REFERENCE: Johnston, 1981.

thawed ground (see also *noncryotic ground; unfrozen ground*)
    [sol dégelé]
Previously *frozen ground* in which all ice has melted.
> COMMENT: *Unfrozen ground* is thawed ground only if it were previously frozen. Thawed ground is commonly noncryotic, but it may be cryotic.
> REFERENCE: van Everdingen, 1976.

thawing (of *frozen ground*)
    [dégel (du gélisol)]
Melting of the ice in *frozen ground*, usually as a result of a rise in temperature.

thawing degree-day (see *degree-day*)

thawing front (see also *freezing front*)
    [front de dégel]
The advancing boundary between *thawed ground* and *frozen ground* (see Figure 4).
> COMMENT: The thawing front may be advancing into cither seasonally or perennially frozen ground during progressive thawing. In *seasonal frost* areas there will be two thawing fronts during the annual thawing period; one moving downward, the other moving upward. The thawing front usually coincides more closely with the position of the 0°C isotherm than the *freezing front* except in *saline permafrost*.
> SYNONYM: frost table.

thawing index (see also *degree-day; n-factor; freezing index*)
    [indice de dégel]
The cumulative number of *degree-days* above 0°C for a given time period.
> COMMENT: Four main types of air thawing indices have been used:
> 1. approximate thawing index – calculated from the mean monthly air temperatures for a specific station without making corrections for negative *degree-days* (below 0°C) in spring and fall (Boyd, 1973, 1979);
> 2. total annual thawing index – calculated by adding all the positive mean daily temperatures (°C) for a specific station during a calendar year (Harris, 1981);
> 3. seasonal thawing index – calculated as the arithmetic sum of all the positive and negative mean daily air temperatures (°C) for a specific station during the time period between the lowest point in the spring and the highest point the next fall on the cumulative degree-day time curve (Huschke, 1959);
> 4. design thawing index – calculated by taking the average of the seasonal thawing indices for the three warmest summers in the most

recent 30 years of record. If data for 30 years are not available, then the index is based on the warmest summer in the latest 10-year period of record (U.S. Army/Air Force, 1966).

The total annual thawing index has been used to predict permafrost distribution, and the design thawing index is commonly used in engineering design to estimate the maximum *depth of thaw* in *frozen ground.*

A surface (ground, pavement, etc.) thawing index differs from the air thawing index (see *n-factor*).

thermal contraction crack (see also *dilation crack; sand wedge; soil wedge;*)
      [fente de contraction thermique]
A tensile fracture resulting from thermal stresses in *frozen ground.*

      COMMENT: Tensile stresses caused by a reduction in ground temperature are probably a major factor in thermal contraction cracking, but it is usually difficult to prove that desiccation is not also involved.

      SYNONYMS: frost crack, frost fissure, and (not recommended) frost wedge, contraction crack.

      REFERENCES: Lachenbruch, 1962, 1966; Washburn, 1979.

thermal erosion
      [érosion thermique]
The erosion of *ice-rich permafrost* by the combined thermal and mechanical action of moving water.

      COMMENT: Thermal erosion is a dynamic process involving the wearing away by thermal means (i.e., the melting of ice), and by mechanical means (i.e., hydraulic transport). Thermal erosion is distinct from the development of *thermokarst terrain*, which results from thermal melting followed by subsidence of the ground but without hydraulic transport of earth materials. An example of the combined thermal and mechanical effects of moving water is the formation of a *thermo-erosional niche.*

      REFERENCES: Walker and Arnborg, 1966; Mackay, 1970; French, 1976; Are, 1978; Newbury et al., 1978.

thermal pile (see also *thermosyphon*)
      [pieu thermique]
A foundation pile on which natural convection or forced circulation cooling systems or devices have been installed to remove heat from the ground (see Figure 24).

      COMMENT: There are two basic types of thermal piles. Passive or natural convection systems use self-powered devices, commonly referred to as *thermosyphons*, or heat pipes, which operate only when air temperatures are lower than the ground temperature. Forced circulation refrigeration systems require external power and mechanical equipment to circulate refrigerants, such as antifreeze liquids, chilled gases or cool air, and may be operated throughout the year or only during the winter. Both types may be fastened to, or form part of, the pile, or, if the pile is a sealed unit (e.g., a steel pipe), the pile itself may serve as a heat-removal device as well as a structural unit.

Thermal piles are used to decrease the time for and ensure *freezeback* of the slurry and ground around piles, to prevent or control long-term *permafrost degradation*, and to decrease the existing ground temperatures around piles, particularly in warm temperature permafrost areas.

REFERENCES: Heuer, 1979; Johnston, 1981.

thermal properties of frozen ground

[propriétés thermiques du gélisol]

The properties of the ground governing the flow of heat through it, and its freezing and thawing conditions.

COMMENT: The position of the interface between thawed and frozen soil with respect to the ground surface, for a given surface-temperature regime, depends on the thermal properties of the strata located above and immediately below the interface. The basic thermal properties of frozen ground are thermal conductivity, heat capacity and latent heat of fusion.

Thermal conductivity is a measure of the quantity of heat that will flow through a unit area of a substance in unit time under a unit temperature gradient.

Heat capacity (specific heat) is the amount of heat required to raise the temperature of a unit mass of a substance by one degree (sensible heat capacity). Volumetric heat capacity is the amount of heat required to raise the temperature of a unit volume of a substance by one degree. It is equal to the heat capacity multiplied by the density. Because the phase change in frozen soils is often gradual and continuous, the term "apparent heat capacity" is introduced to designate the rate of change of the total heat content (sensible plus latent heat) with temperature.

The volumetric latent heat of fusion is the amount of heat required to melt the ice (or freeze the water) in a unit volume of soil. When phase change occurs over a temperature range, the latent heat manifests itself as an apparent (large) increase in heat capacity.

Thermal diffusivity is defined as the ratio of the thermal conductivity to the volumetric heat capacity. It expresses the facility with which a material will undergo temperature change.

These thermal properties vary with phase composition and hence temperature, soil type, water content, porosity, degree of saturation, density and organic content.

REFERENCE: Johnston, 1981.

thermal talik (see *talik*)

thermocirque (not recommended; see *retrogressive thaw slump*)

thermo-erosional cirque (not recommended; see *retrogressive thaw slump*)

thermo-erosional niche
[niche d'érosion thermique]
A recess at the base of a river bank or coastal bluff produced by *thermal erosion* of *ice-rich permafrost* (see Figure 22d).
> COMMENT: A niche may extend more than 10 m into a bank or bluff. Subsequently, the undercut sediments may collapse along a line of weakness, such as an *ice wedge*, destroying the niche. Niche development and bank/bluff collapse is a unique mechanism of erosion in *permafrost regions*. Very rapid coastal or bank retreat can occur if collapse debris is removed by waves or water currents.
> REFERENCES: Walker and Arnborg, 1966; Czudek and Demek, 1970; French, 1976; Are, 1978; Newbury et al., 1978; Harry et al., 1983.

thermokarst (see also *alas/alass; thermokarst terrain*)
[thermokarst]
The process by which characteristic landforms result from the thawing of *ice-rich permafrost*.
> REFERENCES: French, 1976; Washburn, 1979.

thermokarst lake (see also *oriented lake; thaw basin; thermokarst*)
[lac de thermokarst]
A lake occupying a closed depression formed by settlement of the ground following melting of *ground ice* (see Figure 22c).
> COMMENT: Thermokarst lakes are generally shallow. The depressions may expand by *active-layer failure* processes (see *alas*); the lakes may expand by *thermokarst* processes. In glaciated terrain they may be similar in appearance to kettle lakes.
> SYNONYMS: (not recommended) thaw lake, cave-in lake.
> REFERENCES: Wallace, 1948; Hopkins, 1949.

thermokarst mound (see *mound, thermokarst*)

thermokarst terrain (see also *collapse scar; ice-cored topography; thaw sink; thermokarst*)

[modelé de thermokarst]

The irregular topography resulting from the melting of excess *ground ice* and subsequent *thaw settlement* (see Figure 22).

> COMMENT: Except for a *thaw sink* there is little underground drainage in thermokarst terrain. Annual thawing of the *active layer* does not produce thermokarst terrain. The melting of *ground ice* may be initiated by climatic change, destruction of an insulating vegetation cover by fire, animals or man, or by any other disturbance of the *ground thermal regime*, including the acceleration of the rate of thawing by moving water. Morphological features of thermokarst topography include depressions (see also *alas*); lakes (see also *oriented lake; thermokarst lake*); mounds (see *mound, thermokarst*); and small, more or less equidimensional depressions or pits.

> Thermokarst landforms may be divided into active and inactive forms. Inactive thermokarst indicates that thermal equilibrium has been regained, whereas active thermokarst indicates continuing thermal disequilibrium. Thermokarst terrain is so named because of its superficial resemblance to the karst topography typical of limestone regions.

> REFERENCES: Hopkins, 1949; Czudek and Demek, 1970; French, 1976.

thermopile (see *thermal pile*)

thermosyphon (see also *thermal pile*)

[thermosiphon]

A passive heat transfer device installed to remove heat from the ground (see Figure 24).

> COMMENT: Thermosyphons, also called thermotubes or heat pipes, usually consist of a sealed tube containing a liquid or gas. These devices have no moving parts, require no external power for operation, and function only when air temperatures are lower than the ground temperature. They may be either single- or two-phase systems.

> Single-phase devices are usually liquid- or air-filled vertical pipes. During the winter, heat from the soil surrounding the embedded portion of the pipe is absorbed by and thus warms the working fluid, which rises to the above-ground radiator section of the pipe exposed to the cooler air and loses its heat by conduction and natural convection.

> A two-phase device is a sealed tube containing a suitable working fluid (part liquid and part vapour). When the air temperature falls below the ground temperature, the vapour condenses in the radiator section of the tube, the pressure in the tube is reduced and the liquid in the lower section starts to boil. The resulting cycle of boiling, vapour movement up the tube, condensation, and return of the

condensate by gravity flow is an effective way of transferring heat up the tube, thus cooling the ground.
REFERENCES: Long, 1966; Heuer, 1979; Johnston, 1981; Hayley, 1982; Hayley et al., 1983.

thermotube (see *thermosyphon*)

through talik (see *talik*)

thufur (see also *hummock, earth; hummock, turf*)
       [thufur]
A perennial hummock formed in either the *active layer* in permafrost areas or *seasonally frozen ground* in non-permafrost areas, during freezing of the ground (see Figure 20d).

> COMMENT: Thufa (an Icelandic term, plural) can be formed in the warmer part of the zone of *discontinuous permafrost* and also under conditions of maritime *seasonal frost*. The hummock may be as much as 50 cm in height and 160 cm in diameter and can reform within 20 years following destruction. Growth is favoured by silty sediments, a maritime climate and reasonably good drainage.
> REFERENCES: Thorarinsson, 1951; Schunke, 1975; Scotter and Zoltai, 1982.

total water content (see *water content, total*)

transient talik (see *talik*)

tundra
       [toundra]
Treeless terrain, with a continuous cover of vegetation, found at both high latitudes and high altitudes.

> COMMENT: Tundra vegetation comprises lichens, mosses, sedges, grasses, forbs and low shrubs, including heaths, and dwarf willows and birches. This vegetation cover occurs most widely in the zone immediately north of the boreal forest including the treeless parts of the forest-tundra ecotone adjacent to the treeline. In high altitudes, tundra occurs immediately above the forest zone, and the upper altitudinal timberline.
> The term "tundra" is used to refer to both the region and the vegetation growing in the region. It should not be used as an adjective to describe lakes, polygons or other physiographic features.
> Areas of discontinuous vegetation in the polar semi-desert of the High Arctic are better termed "barrens." Unvegetated areas of polar desert may be caused by climatic (too cold or too dry) or edaphic (low soil nutrients or toxic substrate) factors or a combination of both.
> REFERENCE: Polunin, 1951.

tundra hummock (not recommended; see *hummock, earth*; see also *frost mound; tundra*)

tundra polygon (not recommended; see *polygon*; see also *tundra*)

turbic cryosol (see *cryosol*)

turf-banked lobe/terrace (see *solifluction features*; see also *gelifluction*)

turf hummock (see *hummock, turf*)

U

unfrozen ground (see also *frozen ground; noncryotic ground; thawed ground*)
      [sol non gelé]
Soil or rock that does not contain any ice.
      COMMENT: Unfrozen ground can be cryotic (T < 0°C) if *freezing-point* depression prevents freezing of the *pore water* (see figures 2 and 3), or if no water is available to freeze (e.g., in *dry permafrost*). It should not be called *thawed ground*, unless it is known that the ground has previously contained ice.
      REFERENCE: van Everdingen, 1976.

unfrozen water content (see *water content, unfrozen*)

upfreezing (of objects) (not recommended; see *frost jacking*)

upper surface of permafrost (not recommended; see *permafrost table*)

upward freezing (see *freezing front*)

V

vein ice (see *ice, vein*)

W

water, pore (see also *freezing-point depression; ice, pore; water content, unfrozen*)
    [eau interstitielle]
Water occurring in the pores of soils and rocks.
    COMMENT: Pore water includes free water and interfacial (adsorbed) water.
    Free water is that portion of the pore water that is free to move between interconnected pores under the influence of gravity. The temperature at which free water will change phase depends primarily on its dissolved-solids content, which determines *freezing-point depression*. It should be noted that the term "free water" also covers water in fissures, solution channels and other openings in soils or rocks.
    Interfacial water forms transition layers at mineral/water and mineral/water/ice interfaces. The intermolecular forces involved are such that this water does not move under the influence of gravity. The temperature at which any portion of the interfacial water will change phase depends on the total energy of the various adsorption forces, which in turn depend on distance from the mineral surface, type of mineral and solute content of the water.
    REFERENCE: Anderson and Morgenstern, 1973.

water content (see *water content, total*; see also *ice content*)

water content, total (see also *ice, pore; ice content; water, pore; water content, unfrozen*)
    [teneur en eau totale]
The total amount of water (unfrozen water + ice) contained in soil or rock.
    COMMENT: When no ice is present, the total water content is usually referred to as "water content" or "moisture content". The total water content of a soil or rock sample includes free water, interfacial (adsorbed) water, and water absorbed by organic material. Water of crystallization or hydration (e.g., in gypsum) is usually not included.
    The total water content is normally determined in one of two ways:
1. on a dry-weight basis (gravimetric), as the ratio of the mass of the water and ice in a sample to the dry mass of the sample, expressed as a percentage; or
2. on a volume basis (volumetric), as the ratio of the volume of water and ice in a sample to the volume of the whole sample, expressed as a fraction (or, less commonly, as a percentage).

    Because of the way in which it is defined, the volumetric total water content cannot exceed unity, whereas the gravimetric total water content can greatly exceed 100%. During thawing of a sample of *frozen ground* the volumetric total water content decreases, but the gravimetric total water content remains constant.
    REFERENCE: Anderson and Morgenstern, 1973.

water content, unfrozen (see also *ice, pore; ice content; water, pore; water content, total*)

[teneur en eau non gelée]

The amount of unfrozen (liquid) water contained in frozen soil or rock (Figure 3).

> COMMENT: The unfrozen water content can include free water that can be moved by gravity, and/or interfacial (adsorbed) water that cannot be moved by gravity.
>
> The main factors controlling the unfrozen water content in *frozen ground* (or in partially frozen ground) are the specific surface area of mineral particles, mineral type, pore size distribution, dissolved-solids content of the *pore water*, and kind of exchangeable ions. The unfrozen water content at temperatures below 0°C is highest in clays and decreases with decreasing temperature, clay content, and dissolved-solids content, and with increasing particle size. Unfrozen water content, like *total water content*, can be determined either gravimetrically or volumetrically.
>
> SYNONYM: (not recommended) liquid water content.
>
> REFERENCES: Williams, 1967; Penner, 1970; Anderson and Morgenstern, 1973; van Everdingen, 1976.

wedge, composite (see *composite wedge*; see also *ice wedge; ice-wedge cast; sand wedge*)

wedge, ice (see *ice wedge*)

wedge, sand (see *sand wedge*)

wedge, soil (see *soil wedge*)

wedge ice (see *ice, wedge*)

well-bonded permafrost (see *permafrost, ice-bonded*)

widespread permafrost (see *permafrost, discontinuous*)

winter frost (not recommended; see *frost, seasonal*)

Z

zero annual amplitude, depth of (see *depth of zero annual amplitude*)

zero curtain
    [période zéro]
The period of time during which a nearly constant temperature, very close to the freezing point, exists during annual freezing (and occasionally during thawing) of the *active layer* (see Figure 6).

> COMMENT: The zero curtain results from the dissipation of the latent heat of fusion of water during freezing or thawing of the ground. It can persist for several hours or several weeks depending largely on the water content of the ground, snow cover and air temperatures.
> Although the zero curtain can occur in non-permafrost areas, it is most pronounced in permafrost areas, especially during freezing of the *active layer*.
>   The zero curtain is not only evident in freezing and thawing of undisturbed natural terrain but is also an important factor with respect to *frost action*, refreezing of the ground (backfill or slurry) around foundations, etc. and can have a major effect on the thermal regime of the *active layer* and of the permafrost.
> REFERENCES: Muller, 1943; Brewer, 1958; French, 1976; Washburn, 1979.

zone of minimum annual amplitude (not recommended; see *depth of zero annual amplitude*)

zone of zero annual amplitude (not recommended; see *depth of zero annual amplitude*)

References

ANDERSLAND, O.B. and ANDERSON, D.M. (Editors), 1978. *Geotechnical Engineering for Cold Regions.* McGraw-Hill, New York, N.Y., 576 p.

ANDERSON, D.M., GATTO, L.W. and UGOLINI, F., 1973. "An examination of Mariner 6 and 7 imagery for evidence of permafrost terrain on Mars." Proceedings Second International Conference on Permafrost, Yakutsk, U.S.S.R., July 1973, North American Contribution, U.S. National Academy of Sciences, Washington, D.C., pp. 499-508.

ANDERSON, D.M. and MORGENSTERN, N.R., 1973. "Physics, chemistry and mechanics of frozen ground: A review." Proceedings Second International Conference on Permafrost, Yakutsk, U.S.S.R., July 1973, North American Contribution, U.S. National Academy of Sciences, Washington, D.C., pp. 257-288.

ANDERSSON, J.G., 1906. "Solifluction, a component of subaerial denudation." *Journal of Geology,* Vol. 14, pp. 91-112.

ARE, F.E., 1978. "The reworking of shorelines in the permafrost zone." Proceedings Second International Conference on Permafrost, Yakutsk, U.S.S.R., July 1973, U.S.S.R. Contribution, U.S. National Academy of Sciences, Washington, D.C., pp. 59-62.

BARANOV, I.Ya., 1978. "Problems of cryology." Proceedings Second International Conference on Permafrost, Yakutsk, U.S.S.R., July 1973, U.S.S.R. Contribution, U.S. National Academy of Sciences, Washington, D.C., pp. 3-7.

BENEDICT, J.B., 1970. "Downslope soil movement in a Colorado alpine region: rates, processes and climatic significance." *Arctic and Alpine Research,* Vol. 2, No. 3, pp. 165-226.

BERG, T.E. and BLACK, R.F., 1966. "Preliminary measurements of growth of nonsorted polygons, Victoria Land, Antarctica." In: *Antarctic Soils and Soil-Forming Processes* (J.F.S. Tedrow, Editor), American Geophysical Union Antarctic Research Series, U.S. National Academy of Sciences, Washington, D.C., Publication 1418, pp. 61-108.

BILY, C. and DICK, J.W.L., 1974. "Naturally occurring gas hydrates in the Mackenzie Delta, N.W.T." *Bulletin of Canadian Petroleum Geology,* Vol. 22, pp. 340-352.

BLACK, R.F., 1969. "Climatically significant fossil periglacial phenomena in northcentral United States." *Biuletyn Periglacjalny,* 20, pp. 225-238.

BLACK, R.F., 1976. "Features indicative of permafrost." *Annual Review of Earth and Planetary Sciences* (F.A. Donath, Editor). Annual Reviews, Inc., Palo Alto, California, Vol. 4, pp. 75-94.

BLACK, R.F. and BARKSDALE, W.L., 1949. "Oriented lakes of northern Alaska." *Journal of Geology,* Vol. 57, pp. 105-118.

BLACK, R.F. and BERG, T.E., 1966. "Patterned ground in Antarctica." Proceedings Permafrost International Conference, Lafayette, Indiana, November 1963, U.S. National Academy of Sciences, Washington, D.C., Publication No. 1287, pp. 121-128.

BLANCHARD, D. and FRÉMOND, M., 1982. "Cryogenic suction in soils." Proceedings Third International Symposium on Ground Freezing, Hanover, New Hampshire, June 1982, (Vol. 1), pp. 233-238.

BOYD, D.W., 1973. *Normal freezing and thawing degree-days for Canada: 1931-1960.* Environment Canada, Atmospheric Environment Service, Downsview, Ontario, Publication CLI 4-73, 38 p.

BOYD, D.W., 1979. *Degree days: The different types.* National Research Council Canada, Division of Building Research, Ottawa, Building Research Note No. 138, 8 p.

BREWER, M.C., 1958. "Some results of geothermal investigations of permafrost in northern Alaska." *Transactions, American Geophysical Union,* Vol. 39, No. 1, pp. 19-26.

BREWER, R. and PAWLUK, S., 1975. "Investigations of some soils developed in hummocks of the Canadian sub-arctic and southern Arctic regions. 1. Morphology and Micromorphology." *Canadian Journal of Soil Science,* Vol. 55, No. 3, pp. 301-319.

BROWN, J., 1969. "Soils of the Okpilak River Region, Alaska." In: *The Periglacial Environment* (T.L. Péwé, Editor), McGill-Queen's University Press, Montreal, pp. 93-128.

BROWN, R.J.E., 1966. "Permafrost, climafrost, and the muskeg H factor." Proceedings Eleventh Muskeg Research Conference, National Research Council Canada, Associate Committee on Soil and Snow Mechanics, Ottawa, Technical Memorandum No. 87, pp. 159-178.

BROWN, R.J.E., 1967a. "Comparison of permafrost conditions in Canada and the U.S.S.R." *Polar Record,* Vol. 13, No. 87, pp. 741-751.

BROWN, R.J.E., 1967b. Permafrost Map of Canada. National Research Council Canada, Pub. NRC 9769 and Geological Survey of Canada, Map 1246A (with marginal notes).

BROWN, R.J.E., 1970a. "Occurrence of permafrost in Canadian peatlands." Proceedings Third International Peat Congress, Quebec, 1968, National Research Council Canada, Ottawa, pp. 174-181.

BROWN, R.J.E., 1970b. *Permafrost in Canada: Its influence on northern development.* University of Toronto Press, Toronto, 234 p.

BROWN, R.J.E., 1971. "Characteristics of the active layer in the permafrost region of Canada." Proceedings Seminar on Permafrost Active Layer, May 1971, National Research Council Canada, Associate Committee on Geotechnical Research, Ottawa, Technical Memorandum 103, pp. 1-7.

BROWN, R.J.E., 1978. Permafrost Map of Canada. In: *Hydrological Atlas of Canada,* Department of Fisheries and Environment, Ottawa, Canada, Plate No. 32.

BROWN, R.J.E. and KUPSCH, W.O., 1974. *Permafrost Terminology*. National Research Council Canada, Associate Committee on Geotechnical Research, Ottawa, Technical Memorandum No. 111, 62 p.

BRYAN, K., 1946. "Cryopedology – the study of frozen ground and intensive frost action with suggestions on nomenclature." *American Journal of Science*, 244, pp. 622-642.

CANADA SOIL SURVEY COMMITTEE, 1978. *The Canadian System of Soil Classification*. Agriculture Canada, Ottawa, Publication 1646, 164 p.

CAPPS, S.R., Jr., 1910. "Rock glaciers in Alaska." *Journal of Geology*, Vol. 18, pp. 359-375.

CAREY, K.L., 1970. *Icing occurrence, control and prevention: An annotated bibliography*. U.S. Army, C.R.R.E.L., Hanover, New Hampshire, Special Report 151, 57 p.

CAREY, K.L., 1973. *Icings developed from surface water and ground water*. U.S. Army, C.R.R.E.L., Hanover, New Hampshire, Monograph MIII-D3, 67 p.

CARLSON, H. and KERSTEN, M.S., 1953. "Calculation of depths of freezing and thawing under pavements." U.S. National Research Council, Highway Research Board, Bulletin No. 71, pp. 81-98 (includes Discussion by H.P. Aldrich and H.M. Paynter).

CARSON, C.E. and HUSSEY, K.M., 1962. "The oriented lakes of Arctic Alaska." *Journal of Geology*, Vol. 70, pp. 417-439.

CHAMBERLAIN, E.J., 1981. *Frost susceptibility of soil: Review of index tests*. U.S. Army, C.R.R.E.L., Hanover, New Hampshire, Monograph 81-2, 121 p.

CHENG, Guodong, 1983. "The mechanism of repeated-segregation for the formation of thick layered ground ice." *Cold Regions Science and Technology*, Vol. 8, pp. 57-66.

CORTE, A.E., 1962. "Vertical migration of particles in front of a moving freezing plane." *Journal of Geophysical Research*, Vol. 67, pp. 1085-1090.

CZUDEK, T. and DEMEK, J., 1970. "Thermokarst in Siberia and its influence on the development of lowland relief." *Quaternary Research*, Vol. I, pp. 103-120.

DELORME, L.D., ZOLTAI, S.C. and KALAS, L.L., 1978. "Freshwater shelled invertebrate indicators of paleoclimate in northwestern Canada during late glacial times: Reply". *Canadian Journal of Earth Sciences*, Vol. 15, No. 3, pp. 462-463.

DEMEK, J., 1969. "Cryoplanation terraces, their geographical distribution, genesis and development." Ceskoslovenské Akademie Ved Rozprovy, Rada Matematickych a Prirodnich Ved, Vol. 79, No. 4, 80 p.

DOSTOVALOV, B.N. and POPOV, A.I., 1966. "Polygonal systems of ice wedges and conditions of their development." Proceedings Permafrost International Conference, Lafayette, Indiana, November 1963, U.S. National Academy of Sciences, Washington, D.C., Publication 1287, pp. 102-105.

DYKE, L.D., 1981. "Bedrock heave in the central Arctic." Geological Survey of Canada, Ottawa, Paper 81-1A, pp. 157-167.

DYKE, L.D., 1984. "Frost heaving of bedrock in permafrost regions." *Bulletin of the Association of Engineering Geologists*, Vol. 21, No. 4, pp. 389-405.

DYLIK, J., 1964. "Éléments essentiels de la notion de 'périglaciaire'." *Biuletyn Peryglacjalny*, 14, pp. 111-132.

EAKIN, H.M., 1916. "The Yukon-Koyukuk region, Alaska." U.S. Geological Survey, Bulletin No. 631, pp. 67-88.

FANALE, F.P. and CLARK, R.N., 1983. "Solar system ices and Mars permafrost." Proceedings Fourth International Conference on Permafrost, Fairbanks, Alaska, July 1983, National Academy Press, Washington, D.C., pp. 289-294.

FERRIANS, O.J., Jr., KACHADOORIAN, R. and GREENE, G.W., 1969. *Permafrost and related engineering problems in Alaska.* U.S. Geological Survey, Professional Paper 678, 37 p.

FLEMAL, R.C., 1976. "Pingos and pingo scars: Their characteristics, distribution, and utility in reconstructing former permafrost environments." *Quaternary Research*, Vol. 6, No. 1, pp. 37-53.

FOTIEV, S.M., 1978. "Effect of long-term cryometamorphism of earth materials on the formation of groundwater." Proceedings Third International Conference on Permafrost, Edmonton, Alberta, National Research Council Canada, Ottawa, Vol. 1, pp. 181-187 (In Russian). Translation in: English translations of the forty-nine Soviet papers, the one French paper, and the three invited Soviet theme papers, Part I: English translations of twenty-six of the Soviet papers, National Research Council Canada, Ottawa, Publication No. NRCC 18119, 1980, pp. 177-194.

FOX, C.A., 1983. "Micromorphology of an orthic turbic cryosol – a permafrost soil." In: *Soil Micromorphology* (P. Bullock and G.P. Murphy, Editors), A.B. Academic Publishers, Oxford, pp. 699-705.

FRENCH, H.M., 1975. "Man-induced thermokarst development, Sachs Harbour airstrip, Banks Island, N.W.T." *Canadian Journal of Earth Sciences*, Vol. 12, No. 2, pp. 132-144.

FRENCH, H.M., 1976. *The Periglacial Environment.* Longman Group Limited, London and New York, 309 p.

FRENCH, H.M., HARRY, D.G. and CLARK, M.J., 1982. "Ground ice stratigraphy late-Quaternary events, southwest Banks Island, Canadian Arctic." The Roger J.E. Brown Memorial Volume, Proceedings Fourth Canadian Permafrost Conference, Calgary, Alberta, March 1981, National Research Council Canada, Ottawa, pp. 81-90.

FUJII, Y. and HIGUCHI, K., 1978. "Distribution of alpine permafrost in the northern hemisphere and its relation to air temperature." Proceedings Third International Conference on Permafrost, Edmonton, Alberta, July 1978, National Research Council Canada, Ottawa, Vol. 1, pp. 366-371.

FYODOROV, J.S. (compiler) and IVANOV, N.S. (Editor), 1974. *English Russian geocryological dictionary.* Yakutsk State University, Yakutsk, U.S.S.R., 127 p.

GARG, O.P., 1973. "In situ physicomechanical properties of permafrost using geophysical techniques." Proceedings Second International Conference on Permafrost, Yakutsk, U.S.S.R., July 1973, North American Contribution, U.S. National Academy of Sciences, Washington, D.C., pp. 508-517.

GELL, W.A., 1978. "Thermal contraction cracks in massive segregated ice, Tuktoyaktuk Peninsula, N.W.T., Canada." Proceedings Third International Conference on Permafrost, Edmonton, Alberta, July 1978, National Research Council Canada, Ottawa, Vol. 1, pp. 278-281.

GILPIN, R.R., 1982. "A frost heave interface condition for use in numerical modelling." The Roger J.E. Brown Memorial Volume, Proceedings Fourth Canadian Permafrost Conference, Calgary, Alberta, March 1981, National Research Council Canada, Ottawa, pp. 459-465.

GLEN, J.W., 1974. *The physics of ice.* U.S. Army, C.R.R.E.L., Hanover, New Hampshire, Monograph II-C2a, 86 p.

GOLD, L.W., 1967. "Influence of surface conditions on ground temperature." *Canadian Journal of Earth Sciences*, Vol. 4, No. 2, pp. 199-208.

GOLD, L.W. and LACHENBRUCH, A.H., 1973. "Thermal conditions in permafrost: A review of North American literature." Proceedings Second International Conference on Permafrost, Yakutsk, U.S.S.R., July 1973, North American Contribution, U.S. National Academy of Sciences, Washington, D.C., pp. 3-25.

GOODRICH, L.E., 1982. "The influence of snow cover on the ground thermal regime." *Canadian Geotechnical Journal*, Vol. 19, No. 4, pp. 421-432.

GOZDZIK, J., 1973. "Origin and stratigraphic position of periglacial structures in Middle Poland." *Acta Geographica*, 31, pp. 104-117.

HARRIS, S.A., 1979. "Ice caves and permafrost zones in southwest Alberta." *Erdkunde*, 33, pp. 61-70.

HARRIS, S.A., 1981. "Climatic relationships of permafrost zones in areas of low winter snow-cover." *Arctic*, Vol. 36, No. 1, pp. 64-70.

HARRIS, S.A., 1986. "Permafrost distribution, zonation and stability along the Eastern Ranges of the Cordillera of North America." *Arctic*, Vol. 39, No. 1, pp. 29-38.

HARRIS, S.A. and BROWN, R.J.E., 1978. "Plateau Mountain: A case study of alpine permafrost in the Canadian Rocky Mountains." Proceedings Third International Conference on Permafrost, Edmonton, Alberta, July 1978, National Research Council Canada, Ottawa, Vol. 1, pp. 385-391.

HARRIS, S.A. and BROWN, R.J.E., 1982. "Permafrost distribution along the Rocky Mountains in Alberta." The Roger J.E. Brown Memorial Volume, Proceedings Fourth Canadian Permafrost Conference, Calgary, Alberta, March 1981, National Research Council Canada, Ottawa, pp. 59-67.

HARRY, D.G. and FRENCH, H.M., 1983. "The orientation and evolution of thaw lakes, southwest Banks Island, Canadian Arctic." Proceedings Fourth International Conference on Permafrost, Fairbanks, Alaska, July 1983, U.S. National Academy Press, Washington, D.C., pp. 456-461.

HARRY, D.G., FRENCH, H.M. and CLARK, M.J., 1983. "Coastal conditions and processes, Sachs Harbour, southwest Banks Island, western Canadian Arctic." *Zeitschrift für Geomorphologie*, Supplement Band 47, pp. 1-26.

HAYLEY, D.W., 1982. "Application of heat pipes to design of shallow foundations on permafrost." The Roger J.E. Brown Memorial Volume, Proceedings Fourth Canadian Permafrost Conference, Calgary, Alberta, March 1981, National Research Council Canada, Ottawa, pp. 535-544.

HAYLEY, D.W., ROGGENSACK, W.D., JUBIEN, W.E. and JOHNSON, P.V., 1983. "Stabilization of sinkholes on the Hudson Bay Railway." Proceedings Fourth International Conference on Permafrost, Fairbanks, Alaska, July 1983, U.S. National Academy Press, Washington, D.C., pp. 468-473.

HEGINBOTTOM, J.A., 1984. "The mapping of permafrost." *Canadian Geographer*, Vol. 28, No. 1, pp. 78-83.

HENNION, F., 1955. "Frost and permafrost definitions." U.S. National Research Council, Highway Research Board, Washington, D.C., HRB Bulletin 111, pp. 107-110.

HEUER, C.E., 1979. *The application of heat pipes on the Trans-Alaska pipeline.* U.S. Army, C.R.R.E.L., Hanover, New Hampshire, Special Report 79-26, 33 p.

HOPKINS, D.M., 1949. "Thaw lakes and thaw sinks in the Imuruk Lake area, Seward Peninsula, Alaska." *Journal of Geology*, Vol. 57, pp. 119-131.

HOPKINS, D.M., KARLSTROM, T.D. and others, 1955. "Permafrost and ground water in Alaska." U.S. Geological Survey, Professional Paper 264-F, pp. 113-146.

HUGHES, O.L., 1969. *Distribution of open-system pingos in central Yukon Territory with respect to glacial limits.* Geological Survey of Canada, Ottawa, Paper 69-34, 8 p.

HUGHES, O.L., 1972. "Surficial geology and land classification." Proceedings Canadian Northern Pipeline Conference, Ottawa, Ontario, February 1972, National Research Council Canada, Associate Committee on Geotechnical Research, Ottawa, Technical Memorandum No. 104, pp. 17-24.

HUNTER, J.A., 1984. "Geophysical techniques for subsea permafrost investigations." Final Proceedings Fourth International Conference on Permafrost, Fairbanks, Alaska, July 1983, U.S. National Academy Press, Washington, D.C., pp. 88-89.

HUNTER, J.A., JUDGE, A.S., MacAULAY, H.A., GOOD, R.L., GAGNE, R.M. and BURNS, R.A., 1976. *The occurrence of permafrost and frozen sub-seabottom materials in the southern Beaufort Sea.* Environment Canada, Ottawa, Beaufort Sea Technical Report No. 22: Beaufort Sea Project, 174 p.

HUSCHKE, R.E. (Editor), 1959. *Glossary of Meteorology.* American Meteorological Society, 638 p.

HUTCHINSON, J.N., 1968. "Mass movement." In: *Encyclopedia of Geomorphology* (R.W. Fairbridge, Editor), Reinhold Book Corporation, New York, N.Y., pp. 688-689.

JAHN, A., 1975. *Problems of the periglacial zone* (Zagadnienia strefy peryglacjalnej). Warsaw, Panstwowe Wydawnictwo Naukowe, 223 p.

JOHNSTON, G.H. (Editor), 1981. *Permafrost: Engineering Design and Construction.* John Wiley & Sons, Canada Ltd., Toronto, 540 p.

JUDGE, A.S., 1982. "Natural gas hydrates in Canada." The Roger J.E. Brown Memorial Volume, Proceedings Fourth Canadian Permafrost Conference, Calgary, Alberta, March 1981, National Research Council Canada, Ottawa, pp. 320-328.

JUMIKIS, A.R., 1977. *Glossary of terms in thermal soil mechanics.* Rutgers University, New Jersey, Engineering Research Publication No. 57, 155 p.

KAPLAN, I.R., 1974. "Introduction." In: *Natural Gases in Marine Sediments* (I.R. Kaplan, Editor), Plenum Press, New York, N.Y., pp. 1-11.

KING, M.S., BAMFORD, T.S. and KURFURST, P.J., 1974. "Ultrasonic velocity measurements on frozen rocks and soils." Proceedings Symposium on Permafrost Geophysics, Calgary, Alberta, National Research Council Canada, Associate Committee on Geotechnical Research, Ottawa, Technical Memorandum No. 113, pp. 35-42.

KONRAD, J-M. and MORGENSTERN, N.R., 1983. "Frost susceptibility of soils in terms of their segregation potential." Proceedings Fourth International Conference on Permafrost, Fairbanks, Alaska, July 1983, U.S. National Academy Press, Washington, D.C., pp. 660-665.

KONRAD, J-M. and MORGENSTERN, N.R., 1984. "Frost heave prediction of chilled pipelines buried in unfrozen soils." *Canadian Geotechnical Journal,* Vol. 21, No. 1, pp. 100-115.

KRUMME, O., 1935. *Frost und Schnee in ihrer Wirkung auf den Boden im Hochtaunus.* Rhein-Mainische Forschungen, 13, 73 p.

KUDRYAVTSEV, V.A. (Editor), 1978. *Obshcheye merzlotovedeniya (Geokriologiya)* (General permafrost science) In Russian. Izd. 2, (Edu 2) Moskva (Moscow), Izdatel'stvo Moskovskogo Universiteta, (Moscow University Editions), 404 p.

LACHENBRUCH, A.H., 1959. "Periodic heat flow in a stratified medium with application to permafrost problems." U.S. Geological Survey, Bulletin 1083-A, pp. 1-36.

LACHENBRUCH, A.H., 1962. *Mechanics of thermal contraction cracks and ice-wedge polygons in permafrost.* U.S. Geological Survey, Special Paper 70, 69 p.

LACHENBRUCH, A.H., 1966. "Contraction theory of ice-wedge polygons: a qualitative discussion." Proceedings Permafrost International Conference, Lafayette, Indiana, November 1963, U.S. National Academy of Sciences, Washington, D.C., Publication 1287, pp. 63-71.

LADANYI, B., 1972. "An engineering theory of creep of frozen soils." *Canadian Geotechnical Journal*, Vol. 9, No. 1, pp. 63-80.

LADANYI, B., 1981. "Mechanical behaviour of frozen soils." In: Mechanics of Structured Media, Proceedings International Symposium on the Mechanical Behaviour of Structured Media, Ottawa, Canada, May 1981. (A.P.S. Selvadurai, Editor) Part B, Elsevier, Amsterdam, pp. 205-245.

LAWSON, D.E., and BROWN, J., 1978. "Disturbance of permafrost, massive ground ice, and surficial materials." In: *Tundra disturbance and recovery following the 1949 exploratory drilling, Fish Creek, Northern Alaska* by D.E. Lawson et al., U.S. Army, C.R.R.E.L., Hanover, New Hampshire, Report 78-28, pp. 14-24.

LINELL, K.A., and KAPLAR, C.W., 1966. "Description and classification of frozen soils." Proceedings Permafrost International Conference, Lafayette, Indiana, November 1963, U.S. National Academy of Sciences, Washington, D.C., Publication 1287, pp. 481-487.

LINELL, K.A. and LOBACZ, E.F., 1980. *Design and construction of foundations in areas of deep seasonal frost and permafrost.* U.S. Army, C.R.R.E.L., Hanover, New Hampshire, Special Report 80-34, 320 p.

LONG, E.L., 1966. "The Long Thermopile." Proceedings Permafrost International Conference, Lafayette, Indiana, November 1963. U.S. National Academy of Sciences, Washington, D.C., Publication 1287, pp. 487-491.

LUNARDINI, V.J., 1978. "Theory of n-factors and correlation of data." Proceedings Third International Conference on Permafrost, Edmonton, Alberta, July 1978, National Research Council Canada, Ottawa, Vol. 1, pp. 41-46.

LUNARDINI, V.J., 1981. *Heat Transfer in Cold Climates.* Van Nostrand Reinhold, New York, N.Y., 704 p.

LUNDQVIST, J., 1969. "Earth and ice mounds: A terminological discussion." In: *The Periglacial Environment* (T.L. Péwé, Editor), McGill-Queen's University Press, Montreal, pp. 203-215.

MACKAY, J.R., 1965. "Gas-domed mounds in permafrost, Kendall Island, N.W.T." *Geographical Bulletin*, Vol. 7, No. 2, pp. 105-115.

MACKAY, J.R., 1966. "Segregated epigenetic ice and slumps in permafrost, Mackenzie Delta area, N.W.T." *Geographical Bulletin*, Vol. 8, No. 1, pp. 59-80.

MACKAY, J.R., 1970. "Disturbances to the tundra and forest tundra environment of the western Arctic." *Canadian Geotechnical Journal*, Vol. 7, No. 4, pp. 420-432.

MACKAY, J.R., 1971. "The origin of massive icy beds in permafrost, western Arctic coast, Canada." *Canadian Journal of Earth Sciences*, Vol. 8, No. 4, pp. 397-422.

MACKAY, J.R., 1972a. "Offshore permafrost and ground ice, southern Beaufort Sea, Canada." *Canadian Journal of Earth Sciences*, Vol. 9, No. 11, pp. 1550-1561.

MACKAY, J.R., 1972b. "The world of underground ice." *Annals Association American Geographers*, Vol. 62, No. 1, pp. 1-22.

MACKAY, J.R., 1973a. "Problems in the origin of massive icy beds, western Arctic coast, Canada." Proceedings Second International Conference on Permafrost, Yakutsk, U.S.S.R., July 1973, North American Contribution, U.S. National Academy of Sciences, Washington, D.C., pp. 223-228.

MACKAY, J.R., 1973b. "The growth of pingos, western Arctic coast, Canada." *Canadian Journal of Earth Sciences*, Vol. 10, No. 6, pp. 979-1004.

MACKAY, J.R., 1974a. "Measurement of upward freezing above permafrost with a self-positioning thermistor probe." Geological Survey of Canada, Ottawa, Paper 74-1, Part B, pp. 250-251.

MACKAY, J.R., 1974b. "Reticulate ice veins in permafrost, northern Canada." *Canadian Geotechnical Journal*, Vol. 11, No. 2, pp. 230-237.

MACKAY, J.R., 1975. "Relict ice wedges, Pelly Island, N.W.T." Geological Survey of Canada, Ottawa, Paper 75-1, pp. 469-470.

MACKAY, J.R., 1978. "Freshwater shelled invertebrate indicators of paleoclimate in northwestern Canada during late glacial times: Discussion." *Canadian Journal of Earth Sciences*, Vol. 15, No. 3, pp. 461-462.

MACKAY, J.R., 1979. "Pingos of the Tuktoyaktuk Peninsula area, Northwest Territories." *Géographie physique et Quaternaire*, Vol. 33, No. 1, pp. 3-61.

MACKAY, J.R., 1980. "The origin of hummocks, western Arctic coast, Canada." *Canadian Journal of Earth Sciences*, Vol. 17, No. 8, pp. 996-1006.

MACKAY, J.R., 1983. "Downward water movement into frozen ground, western Arctic coast, Canada." *Canadian Journal of Earth Sciences*, Vol. 20, No. 1, pp. 120-134.

MACKAY, J.R., 1985. "Pingo ice of the western Arctic coast, Canada." *Canadian Journal of Earth Sciences*, Vol. 22, No. 10, pp. 1452-1464.

MACKAY, J.R., and BLACK, R.F., 1973. "Origin, composition, and structure of perennially frozen ground and ground ice: A review." Proceedings Second International Conference on Permafrost, Yakutsk, U.S.S.R., July 1973, North American Contribution, U.S. National Academy of Sciences, Washington, D.C., pp. 185-192.

MACKAY, J.R. and MACKAY, D.K., 1976. "Cryostatic pressures in nonsorted circles (mud hummocks), Inuvik, Northwest Territories." *Canadian Journal Earth Sciences*, Vol. 13, No. 7, pp. 889-897.

MACKAY, J.R. and MATHEWS, W.H., 1974. "Needle ice striped ground." *Arctic and Alpine Research*, Vol. 6, No. 1, pp. 79-84.

MACKAY, J.R. and MATTHEWS, J.V., Jr., 1983. "Pleistocene ice and sand wedges, Hooper Island, Northwest Territories." *Canadian Journal of Earth Sciences*, Vol. 20, No. 7, pp. 1087-1097.

MACKAY, J.R., RAMPTON, V.N. and FYLES, J.G., 1972. "Relic pleistocene permafrost, western Arctic, Canada." *Science*, Vol. 176, pp. 1321-1323.

MCROBERTS, E.C. and MORGENSTERN, N.R., 1974. "The stability of thawing slopes." *Canadian Geotechnical Journal*, Vol. 11, No. 4, pp. 447-469.

MILLER, R.D., 1972. *Freezing and heaving of saturated and unsaturated soils*. U.S. National Research Council, Washington, D.C., Highway Research Record, No. 393, pp. 1-11.

MORGENSTERN, N.R. and NIXON, J.F., 1971. "One-dimensional consolidation of thawing soils." *Canadian Geotechnical Journal*, Vol. 8, No. 4, pp. 558-565.

MÜLLER, F., 1959. *Beobachtungen über Pingos*. Detailuntersuchungen in Ostgrönland und in der kanadischen Arktis: Meddelelser om Grønland, Vol. 153, No. 3, 127 p. *Observations on Pingos*. Translation published by National Research Council Canada, Ottawa, Technical Translation 1073, 1963, 117p.

MULLER, S.W., 1943. *Permafrost or permanently frozen ground and related engineering problems*. U.S. Engineers Office, Strategic Engineering Study, Special Report No. 62, 136 p. (Reprinted in 1947, J.W. Edwards, Ann Arbor, Michigan, 231 p.)

NEWBURY, R.W., BEATY, K.G. and McCULLOUGH, G.K., 1978. "Initial shoreline erosion in a permafrost affected reservoir, Southern Indian Lake, Canada." Proceedings Third International Conference on Permafrost, Edmonton, Alberta, July 1978, National Research Council Canada, Ottawa, Vol. 1, pp. 833-839.

NIXON, J.F., 1982. "Frost heave predictions using the segregation potential concept." *Canadian Geotechnical Journal*, Vol. 19, No. 4, pp. 526-529.

NIXON, J.F. and MORGENSTERN, N.R., 1973. "The residual stress in thawing soils." *Canadian Geotechnical Journal*, Vol. 10, No. 4, pp. 571-580.

OSTERKAMP, T.E. and PAYNE, M.W., 1981. "Estimates of permafrost thickness from well logs in northern Alaska." *Cold Regions Science and Technology*, Vol. 5, No. 1, pp. 13-27.

PAWLUK, S. and BREWER, R., 1975. "Micromorphological and analytical characteristics of some soils from Devon and King Christian Islands, N.W.T." *Canadian Journal of Soil Science*, Vol. 55, No. 3, pp. 349-361.

PENNER, E., 1967. "Pressures developed during the uni-directional freezing of water-saturated porous materials." Proceedings International Conference on Low Temperature Science, Sapporo, Japan, 1966, Vol. 1, Part 2, pp. 1401-1412.

PENNER, E., 1968. "Particle size as a basis for predicting frost action in soils." *Soils and Foundations*, Vol. 8, No. 4, pp. 21-29.

PENNER, E., 1970. "Thermal conductivity of frozen soils." *Canadian Journal of Earth Sciences*, Vol. 7, No. 3, pp. 982-987.

PENNER, E., 1972. "Soil moisture redistribution by ice lensing in freezing soils." Proceedings 17th Annual Meeting, Canadian Society of Soil Science, Lethbridge, Alberta, July 1971, pp. 44-62.

PÉWÉ, T.L., 1954. "Effect of permafrost upon cultivated fields." U.S. Geological Survey, Bulletin 989-F, pp. 315-351.

PÉWÉ, T.L., 1983. "Alpine permafrost in the contiguous United States: A review." *Arctic and Alpine Research*, Vol. 15, No. 2, pp. 145-156.

PIHLAINEN, J.A. and JOHNSTON, G.H., 1963. *Guide to a field description of permafrost*. National Research Council Canada, Associate Committee on Soil and Snow Mechanics, Ottawa, Technical Memorandum No. 79, 21 p.

PISSART, A. and FRENCH, H.M., 1976. "Pingo investigations, north central Banks Island, Canadian Arctic." *Canadian Journal of Earth Sciences*, Vol. 13, No. 7, pp. 937-946.

POLLARD, W.H. and FRENCH, H.M., 1980. "A first approximation of the volume of ground ice, Richards Island, Pleistocene Mackenzie Delta, Northwest Territories, Canada." *Canadian Geotechnical Journal*, Vol. 17, No. 4, pp. 509-516.

POLLARD, W.H. and FRENCH, H.M., 1984. "The groundwater hydraulics of seasonal frost mounds, North Fork Pass, Yukon Territory." *Canadian Journal of Earth Sciences*, Vol. 21, No. 10, pp. 1073-1081.

POLUNIN, N., 1951. "The real Arctic; suggestions for its delimitation, subdivision, and characteristics." *Journal of Ecology*, Vol. 39, pp. 308-315.

POPPE, V. and BROWN, R.J.E., 1976. *Russian-English glossary of permafrost terms*. National Research Council Canada, Associate Committee on Geotechnical Research, Ottawa, Technical Memorandum No. 117, 25 p.

PORSILD, A.E., 1938. "Earth mounds in unglaciated Arctic northwest America." *Geographical Review*, 28, pp. 46-58.

PRICE, W.A., 1968. "Oriented lakes." In: *Encyclopedia of Geomorphology* (R.W. Fairbridge, Editor), Reinhold Book Corporation, New York, N.Y., pp. 784-796.

RAMPTON, V.N., 1974. "The influence of ground ice and thermokarst upon the geomorphology of the Mackenzie-Beaufort region." In: *Research in Polar and Alpine Geomorphology* (B.D. Fahey and R.D. Thompson, Editors), Proceedings 3rd Guelph Symposium on Geomorphology, pp. 43-59.

RAMPTON, V.N. and MACKAY, J.R., 1971. *Massive ice and icy sediments throughout the Tuktoyaktuk Peninsula, Richards Island, and nearby areas, District of Mackenzie.* Geological Survey of Canada, Ottawa, Paper 71-21, 16 p.

RAMPTON, V.N. and WALCOTT, R.I., 1974. "Gravity profiles across ice-cored topography." *Canadian Journal of Earth Sciences*, Vol. 11, No. 1, pp. 110-122.

RAPP, A. and Clark, G.M., 1971. "Large nonsorted polygons in Padjelanta National Park, Swedish Lappland." *Geografiska Annaler*, 53A, pp. 71-85.

RAUP, H.M., 1966. "Turf hummocks in the Mesters Vig District, Northeast Greenland." Proceedings Permafrost International Conference, Lafayette, Indiana, November 1963, U.S. National Academy of Sciences, Washington, D.C., Publication 1287, pp. 43-50.

REGER, R.D. and PÉWÉ, T.L., 1976. "Cryoplanation terraces: indicators of a permafrost environment." *Quaternary Research*, Vol. 6, pp. 99-109.

REX, R.W., 1961. "Hydrodynamic analysis of circulation and orientation of lakes in northern Alaska." In: *Geology of the Arctic* (G.O. Raasch, Editor), University of Toronto Press, Toronto, Vol. 2, pp. 1021-1043.

SAVAGE, C.N., 1968. "Mass wasting." In: *Encyclopedia of Geomorphology* (R.W. Fairbridge, Editor), Reinhold Book Corporation, New York, N.Y., pp. 696-700.

SCHUNKE, E., 1975. *Die Periglazialerscheinungen Islands in Abhängigkeit von Klima und Substrat.* Akad. Wiss. Göttingen Abh., Math.-Phys. Kl. Folge 3, 30, 273 p.

SCOTTER, G.W. and ZOLTAI, S.C., 1982. "Earth hummocks in the Sunshine area of the Rocky Mountains, Alberta and British Columbia." *Arctic*, Vol. 35, No. 3, pp. 411-416.

SELLMANN, P.V., BROWN J., LEWELLEN, R.I., MCKIM, H. and MERRY, C., 1975. *The classification and geomorphic implications of thaw lakes on the Arctic coastal plain, Alaska.* U.S. Army, C.R.R.E.L., Hanover, New Hampshire, Research Report 344, 24 p.

SELLMANN, P.V. and HOPKINS, D.M., 1984. "Subsea permafrost distribution on the Alaskan shelf." Final Proceedings Fourth International Conference on Permafrost, Fairbanks, Alaska, July 1983, U.S. National Academy Press, Washington, D.C., pp. 75-82.

SEPPÄLÄ, M., 1972. "The term 'palsa'." *Zeitschrift für Geomorphologie, N.F. 16, p. 463.*

SHILTS, W.W., 1978. "Nature and genesis of mudboils, central Keewatin, Canada." *Canadian Journal of Earth Sciences,* Vol. 15, No. 7, pp. 1053-1068.

SOLOVIEV, P.A., 1973. "Thermokarst phenomena and landforms due to frost heaving in Central Yakutia." *Biuletyn Peryglacjalny,* 23, pp. 135-155.

STANEK, W., 1977. "A list of terms and definitions." Appendix to: *Muskeg and The Northern Environment in Canada,* University of Toronto Press, Toronto, Ontario, pp. 367-382.

STANEK, W. and WORLEY, I.A., 1983. "A terminology of virgin peat and peatlands." Proceedings International Symposium on Peat Utilization (C.H. Fuchsman and S.A. Spigarelli, Editors), Bemidji State University, Bemidji, Minnesota, October 1983, pp. 75-102.

STEARNS, S.R., 1966. *Permafrost (perennially frozen ground).* U.S. Army, C.R.R.E.L., Hanover, New Hampshire, Monograph I-A2, 77 p.

SWINZOW, G.K., 1966. "Tunneling and subsurface installations in permafrost." Proceedings Permafrost International Conference, Lafayette, Indiana, November 1963, U.S. National Academy of Sciences, Washington, D.C., Publication 1287, pp. 519-526.

TABER, S., 1929. "Frost heaving." *Journal of Geology,* Vol. 37, pp. 428-461.

TARNOCAI, C., 1973. *Soils of the Mackenzie River area.* Indian and Northern Affairs Canada, Environmental- Social Program, Northern Pipelines, Task Force on Northern Oil Development, Ottawa, Report No. 73-26, 136 p.

TARNOCAI, C., 1980. "Summer temperatures of cryosolic soils in the north-central Keewatin, N.W.T." *Canadian Journal of Soil Science,* Vol. 60, No. 2, pp. 311-327.

TARNOCAI, C. and Zoltai, S.C., 1978. "Earth hummocks of the Canadian Arctic and Subarctic." *Arctic and Alpine Research,* Vol. 10, No. 3, pp. 581-594.

THORARINSSON, A., 1951. "Notes on patterned ground in Iceland, with particular reference to the Icelandic 'flas'." *Geografiska Annaler,* Vol. 33, pp. 144-156.

THORN, C.E., 1976. "A model of stoney earth circle development, Schefferville, Quebec." Association of American Geographers, Proceedings, Vol. 8, pp. 19-23.

TOLSTIKHIN, N.I., and TOLSTIKHIN, O.N., 1974. "Groundwater and surface water in the permafrost region." Chapter IX, *General Permafrost Studies* (P.I. Melnikov and O.N. Tolstikhin, Editors), U.S.S.R. Academy of Sciences, Novosibirsk. English translation published by Environment Canada, Inland Waters Directorate, Ottawa, Technical Bulletin No. 97, 1976, 25 p.

TSYTOVICH, N.A., 1973. *Mekhanika Merzlykh gruntov (The mechanics of frozen ground)*, Vysshaya Shkola Press, Moscow (In Russian), 446 p. Translation by Scripta Technica (G.K. Swinzow and G.P. Tschebotarioff, Editors), Scripta/McGraw-Hill, New York, N.Y., 1975, 426 p.

U.S.S.R., 1969. (S.S. VYALOV, and G.V. PORKHAEV, Editors). *Handbook for the design of bases and foundations of buildings and other structures on permafrost.* National Research Council Canada, Canada Institute for Scientific and Technical Information, Ottawa, Technical Translation TT-1865, 1976, 286 p.

U.S.S.R., 1973. (SARKISYAN et al., Editors). *Handbook on the determination of the physical, thermal and mechanical properties of frozen soils.* National Research Council Canada, Canada Institute for Scientific and Technical Information, Ottawa, Technical Translation TT-2064, 1983, 202 p.

U.S. ARMY/AIR FORCE, 1966. *Arctic and subarctic construction: general provisions.* Technical Manual TM-852-1/AFM 88-19, Chapter 1, 48 p.

van EVERDINGEN, R.O., 1976. "Geocryological terminology." *Canadian Journal of Earth Sciences*, Vol. 13, No. 6, pp. 862-867.

van EVERDINGEN, R.O., 1978. "Frost mounds at Bear Rock, near Fort Norman, N.W.T., 1975-1976." *Canadian Journal of Earth Sciences*, Vol. 15, No. 2, pp. 263-276.

van EVERDINGEN, R.O., 1985. "Unfrozen permafrost and other taliks." Workshop on Permafrost Geophysics, Golden, Colorado, October 1984 (J. Brown, M.C. Metz, P. Hoekstra, Editors). U.S. Army, C.R.R.E.L., Hanover, New Hampshire, Special Report 85-5, pp. 101-105.

VINSON, T.S., 1978. "Parameter effects on dynamic properties of frozen soils." American Society of Civil Engineers, Journal Geotechnical Engineering Division, Vol. 104, No. GT10, pp. 1289-1306.

VYALOV, S.S., 1959. *Rheological properties and bearing capacity of frozen soils.* U.S. Army, C.R.R.E.L., Hanover, New Hampshire, Translation 74, 1965, 219 p.

WALKER, H.J. and Arnborg, L., 1966. "Permafrost and ice-wedge effect on riverbank erosion." Proceedings Permafrost International Conference, Lafayette, Indiana, November 1963, U.S. National Academy of Sciences, Washington, D.C., Publication 1287, pp. 164-171.

WALLACE, R.F., 1948. "Cave-in lakes in the Nabesna, Chisana and Tanana River valleys, eastern Alaska." *Journal of Geology*, Vol. 56, pp. 171-181.

WASHBURN, A.L., 1956. "Classification of patterned ground and review of suggested origins." *Bulletin Geological Society of America*, Vol. 67, pp. 823-865.

WASHBURN, A.L., 1973. *Periglacial processes and environments.* Edward Arnold, London, 320 p.

WASHBURN, A.L., 1979. *Geocryology.* Edward Arnold, London, 406 p.

WASHBURN, A.L., 1980. "Permafrost features as evidence of climatic change." *Earth Science Reviews*, Vol. 15, pp. 327-402.

WASHBURN, A.L., 1983. "What is a Palsa?" In: *Mesoformen des Reliefs im Heutigen Periglazialraum* (H. Poser and E. Schunke, Editors), Gottingen, Abhandlungen der Akademie der Wissenschaften in Gottingen, Mathematisch – Physikalische Klasse, Dritte Folge Nr. 35, pp. 34-47.

WHITE, S.E., 1976a. "Is frost action really only hydration shattering? A Review." *Arctic and Alpine Research*, Vol. 8, No. 1, pp. 1-6.

WHITE, S.E., 1976b. "Rock glaciers and blockfields. Review and new data." *Quaternary Research*, Vol. 6, pp. 77-97.

WILLIAMS, J.R., 1965. *Ground water in permafrost regions: An annotated bibliography.* U.S. Geological Survey, Water-Supply Paper 1792, 294 p.

WILLIAMS, J.R., 1970. *Ground water in the permafrost regions of Alaska.* U.S. Geological Survey, Professional Paper 696, 83 p.

WILLIAMS, P.J., 1967. *Properties and behaviour of freezing soils.* Norwegian Geotechnical Institute, Publication No. 72, 119 p.

ZOLTAI, S.C., 1971. "Southern limit of permafrost features in peat landforms, Manitoba and Saskatchewan." Geological Association of Canada, Special Paper No. 9, pp. 305-310.

ZOLTAI, S.C., 1972. "Palsas and peat plateaus in central Manitoba and Saskatchewan." *Canadian Journal of Forest Research*, Vol. 2, No. 3, pp. 291-302.

ZOLTAI, S.C., 1975. "Tree ring record of soil movements on permafrost." *Arctic and Alpine Research*, Vol. 7, No. 4, pp. 331-340.

ZOLTAI, S.C., and POLLETT, F.C., 1983. "Wetlands in Canada: Their classification, distribution, and use." In: *Mires, Swamp, Bog, Fen and Moor, Regional Studies* (A.J.P. Gore, Editor), Elsevier Scientific Publishing Company, Amsterdam, pp. 245-268.

ZOLTAI, S.C., and TARNOCAI, C., 1971. "Properties of a wooded palsa in Northern Manitoba." *Arctic and Alpine Research*, Vol. 3, No. 2, pp. 115-119.

ZOLTAI, S.C. and TARNOCAI, C., 1975. "Perennially frozen peatlands in the western Arctic and Subarctic of Canada." *Canadian Journal of Earth Sciences*, Vol. 12, No. 1, pp. 28-43.

Illustrations

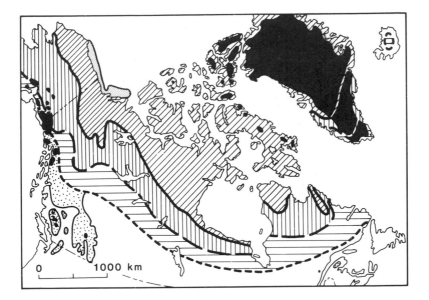

	Zone of *continuous permafrost* (>80% of area underlain by permafrost).
——	Southern boundary of the zone of *continuous permafrost*.
	Zone of *discontinuous permafrost*: subzone of widespread discontinuous permafrost (30 to 80% of area underlain by permafrost).
— —	Boundary between widespread and sporadic *discontinuous permafrost*.
	Zone of *discontinuous permafrost*: subzone of sporadic discontinuous permafrost (<30% of area underlain by permafrost).
– – –	Southern boundary of the *permafrost region*.
	Alpine permafrost.
——	*Alpine permafrost* limit.
	Known *subsea permafrost*.
	Perennial ice caps.

Figure 1 Permafrost in Canada (after Harris, 1986; Heginbottom, 1984; Johnston, 1981)

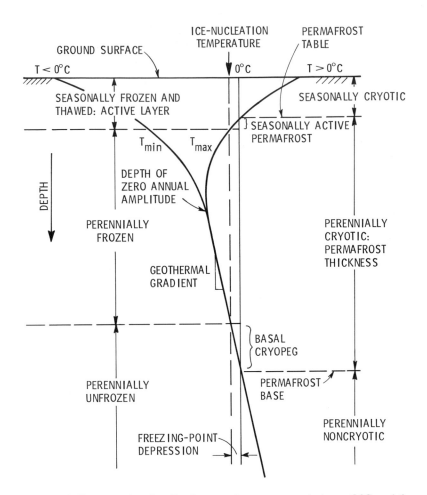

Figure 2 Terms used to describe the ground temperature relative to O°C, and the state of the water versus depth, in a permafrost environment (modified from van Everdingen, 1985)

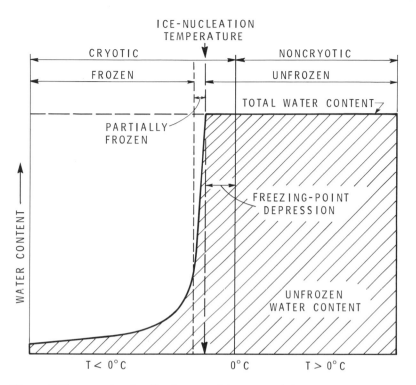

Figure 3 Terms used to describe the state of the water relative to ground temperature in soil materials subjected to freezing temperatures (modified from van Everdingen, 1985)

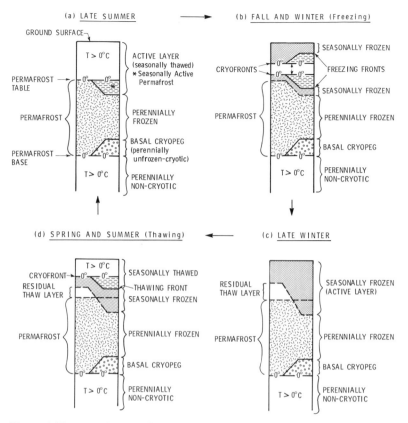

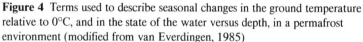

Figure 4 Terms used to describe seasonal changes in the ground temperature relative to 0°C, and in the state of the water versus depth, in a permafrost environment (modified from van Everdingen, 1985)

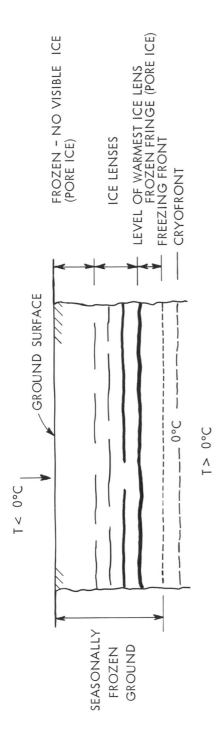

Figure 5 Diagram showing the relative positions of the *frozen fringe*, the *freezing front* and the *cryofront* during freezing of a fine-grained, *frost-susceptible soil*

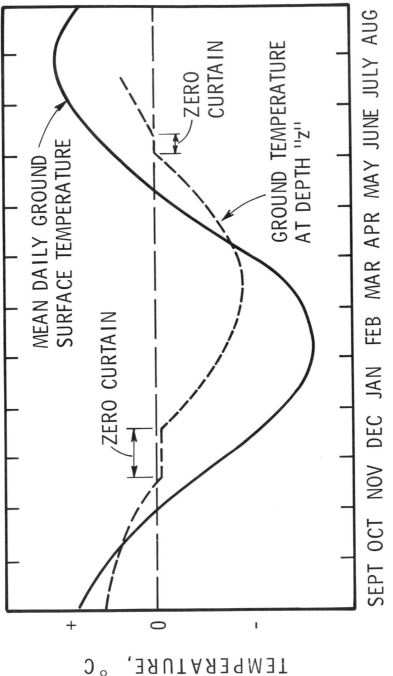

Figure 6 Diagram illustrating the *zero curtain*

118

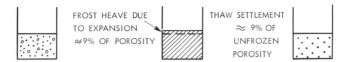

UNFROZEN   FROZEN   THAWED

(a) CLOSED-SYSTEM FREEZING

FROST HEAVE DUE
TO EXPANSION
≈ 9% OF POROSITY

THAW SETTLEMENT
≈ 9% OF
UNFROZEN
POROSITY

(b) OPEN-SYSTEM FREEZING, COARSE-GRAINED SOIL

NO FROST HEAVE;
EXPULSION OF UP
TO 9% OF ORIGINAL
WATER CONTENT

NO THAW
SETTLEMENT

(c) OPEN-SYSTEM FREEZING, FINE-GRAINED SOIL

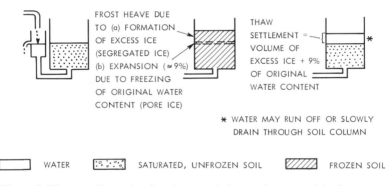

FROST HEAVE DUE
TO (a) FORMATION
OF EXCESS ICE
(SEGREGATED ICE)
(b) EXPANSION (≈ 9%)
DUE TO FREEZING
OF ORIGINAL WATER
CONTENT (PORE ICE)

THAW
SETTLEMENT =
VOLUME OF
EXCESS ICE + 9%
OF ORIGINAL
WATER CONTENT

* WATER MAY RUN OFF OR SLOWLY
DRAIN THROUGH SOIL COLUMN

☐ WATER   ▣ SATURATED, UNFROZEN SOIL   ▨ FROZEN SOIL

Figure 7 Diagrams illustrating *frost heave* and *thaw settlement* resulting from *closed-* and *open-system freezing* of soil materials and the formation of *excess ice*

119

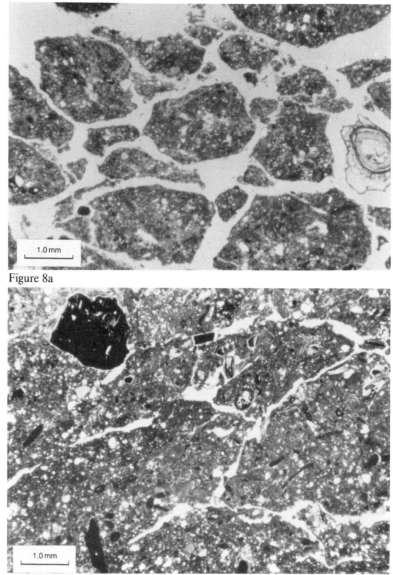

Figure 8a

Figure 8b

Figure 8 *Cryogenic fabrics*, as seen in thin sections (Photos by C.A. Fox, Agriculture Canada, except for (c) by C. Tarnocai, Agriculture Canada).

(a) Discrete, rounded to subangular, units of soil material, granic fabric, at the 0 to 30 cm depth of a Brunisolic Turbic Cryosol developed in an *earth hummock* formed on an undulating morainal till deposit in the Mackenzie Plain, N.W.T. Plane-polarized light, vertical section.

(b) Planar voids resulting from the coalescence of discrete units at their contact points (fragmoidic fabric). Observed within permafrost at a depth of 25 to 38 cm in an Orthic Turbic Cryosol developed in an *earth hummock* formed on a rolling morainal till in the Mackenzie Plain near Carcajou River, N.W.T. Plane polarized light, vertical section.

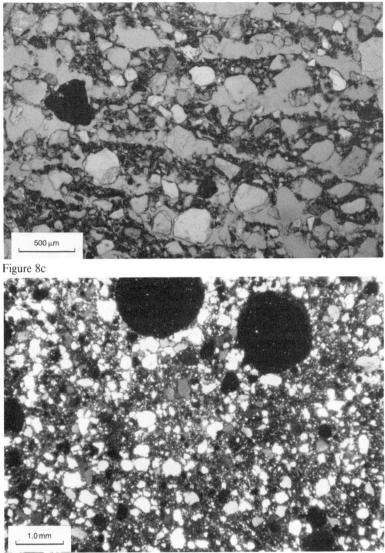

Figure 8c

Figure 8d

Figure 8 (continued)

(c) Banded fabric showing a gradation of fine-to-coarse particle sizes within each layer. Observed within the *active layer* at approximately 30 cm in an Orthic Turbic Cryosol. This soil was developed in a small *polygon* formed on rolling terrain near Goodsir Inlet, Bathurst Island, N.W.T. Partially crossed nicols, vertical section.

(d) Coarse-sized particles form a circular to ellipsoidal pattern referred to as orbiculic fabric. The large circular black regions are pore space (vesicular pores). Observed at a depth of 0 to 20 cm in an Orthic Turbic Cryosol developed in a non-sorted circle on an unglaciated colluvial deposit of the Carcajou Range (Mackenzie Mountains) N.W.T. Crossed nicols, vertical section.

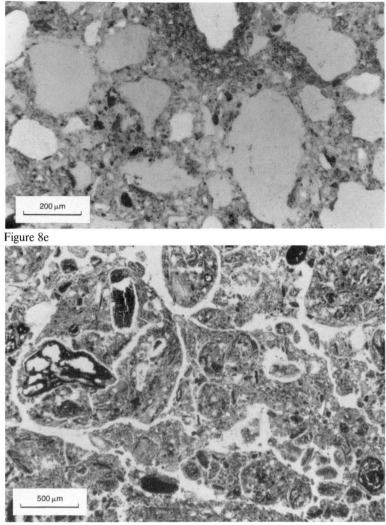

200 μm

Figure 8e

500 μm

Figure 8f
Figure 8 (continued)

(e) Coarse-sized particles showing a tendency to be vertically or nearly vertically aligned (suscitic fabric). Some of the particles are also associated with surface accumulations of finer material. Observed at a depth of 0 to 20 cm in an Orthic Turbic Cryosol in a non-sorted circle on an unglaciated colluvial deposit of the Carcajou Range (Mackenzie Mountains) N.W.T. Partially crossed nicols, vertical section.

(f) Cryogenic processes have formed a complex morphology (conglomeric fabric) in which discrete fragments and rounded units are displaced, then enclosed by finer material and subjected to ice lens formation as evidenced by the associated planar voids. Observed within permafrost at a depth of 31 to 65 cm in a Gleysolic Turbic Cryosol developed in an *earth hummock* on a morainal till deposit in the Horn Plateau Region, N.W.T. Plane-polarized light, vertical section.

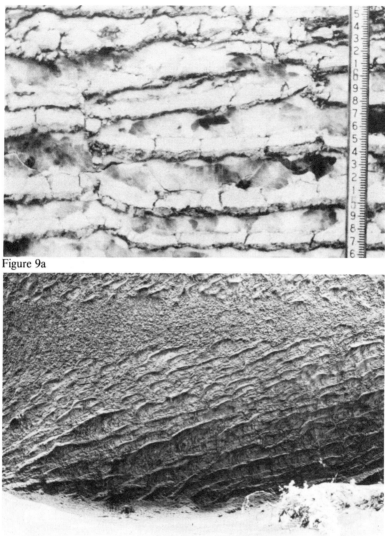

Figure 9a

Figure 9b

Figure 9 Examples of *cryostructures* in frozen ground

(a) *Segregated ice* in varved glaciolacustrine silt clays, Thompson, Manitoba (Photo by G.H. Johnston, National Research Council of Canada)

(b) Inclined *ice lenses*, 30 to 80 cm long and 5 to 10 cm thick, formed by subaqueous syngenetic freezing of glaciolacustrine silty clay near Mayo, Yukon Territory (Photo by H.M. French, University of Ottawa)

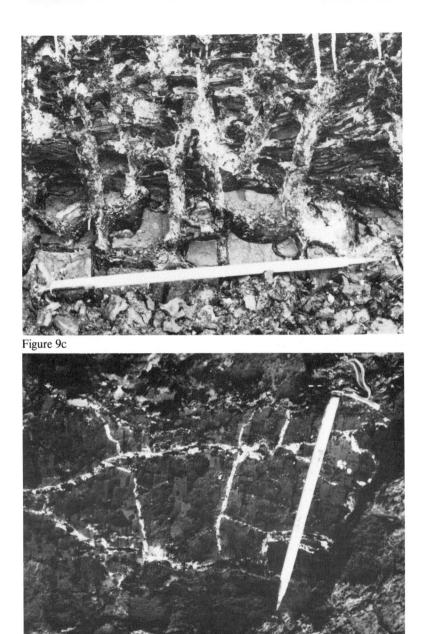

Figure 9c

Figure 9d
Figure 9 (continued)

(c) Coarse reticulate network of *ice veins* formed in glaciolacustrine clay, Sabine Point, Beaufort Sea coastal plain, Yukon Territory (Photo by D.G. Harry, Geological Survey of Canada)

(d) Fine reticulate network of *ice veins* formed in silty clay diamicton, Pelly Island, Mackenzie Delta, N.W.T. (Photo by H.M. French, University of Ottawa)

Figure 10a

Figure 10b

Figure 10 Examples of types of *ground ice*

(a) *Aggradational ice* at the top of permafrost and exposed at the 2 m depth in a pipeline trench, approximately 98 km south of Norman Wells, N.W.T. (Photo by D.G. Harry, Geological Survey of Canada)

(b) Ice (*dilation crack ice?*) between the ice core and heaved, silty, gravelly overburden of a collapsed *pingo*, Thomsen River, north central Banks Island, N.W.T. (Photo by H.M. French, University of Ottawa)

Figure 10c

Figure 10d

Figure 10 (continued)

(c) Columnar ice crystals in a 10 to 20 cm thick layer of *intrusive ice* from within a seasonal *frost blister*, North Fork Pass, Ogilvie Mountains, Yukon Territory (Photo by W.H. Pollard, Memorial University)

(d) *Massive ice* exposed at Peninsula Point, 5 km southwest of Tuktoyaktuk, Mackenzie Delta, N.W.T. (Photo by H.M. French, University of Ottawa)

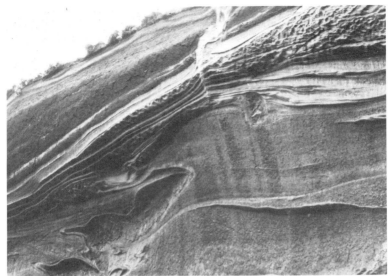

Figure 10e

Figure 10f

Figure 10 (continued)

(e) Glacially deformed *massive ice* exposed on north coast of Pelly Island,
Mackenzie Delta, N.W.T. The exposure is approximately 7 to 10 m high.
(Photo by D.G. Harry, Geological Survey of Canada)

(f) *Massive ice* body near Sabine Point, Beaufort Sea coastal plain, Yukon
Territory (Photo by H.M. French, University of Ottawa)

Figure 10g

Figure 10h
Figure 10 (continued)

(g) *Needle ice* exposed after removal of a stone, Boutillier Pass, Alaska Highway, Yukon Territory (Photo by S.A. Harris, University of Calgary)

(h) Large body of *pingo ice* exposed near summit of a small growing *pingo*, 3 km west of Tuktoyaktuk, Mackenzie Delta, N.W.T. (Photo by H.M. French, University of Ottawa)

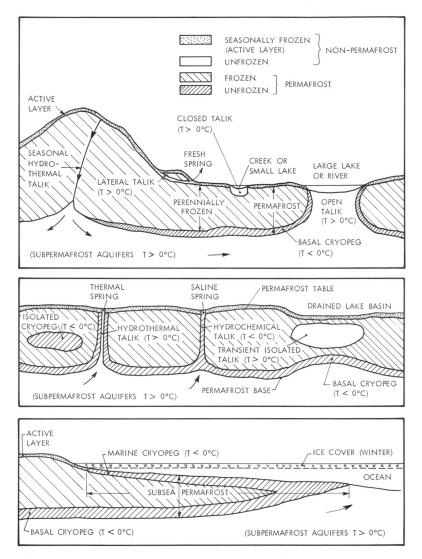

Figure 11 Cross sections illustrating terms used to describe unfrozen zones in a permafrost environment and their relationships with surface water and groundwater flow (modified from van Everdingen, 1976)

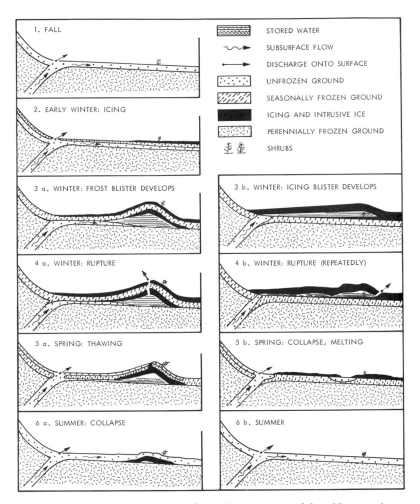

Figure 12 Sequence of events in the formation and decay of *frost blisters* and *icing blisters* (modified from van Everdingen, 1978)

Figure 13a

Figure 13b

Figure 13c

Figure 13 Seasonal *frost mounds* at Bear Rock, near Ft. Norman, N.W.T. (Photos by R.O. van Everdingen, Environment Canada)

(a) *Frost blister* in early July, after melting of snow and the surrounding *icing*

(b) The same *frost blister* in early September, after thawing of the seasonally frozen soil cover and partial collapse of the *intrusive ice* into the drained cavity

(c) Drained cavity (up to 40 cm high) exposed below cut away *intrusive ice* in one of the *frost blisters* (cut at left is about 60 cm high)

Figure 13d

Figure 13e
Figure 13 (continued)

(d) Ruptured and partially collapsed *icing blister* in March (drained cavity was 90 cm high); note smaller *icing blister* in foreground

(e) Block of layered icing ice and massive *intrusive ice* from a ruptured *icing blister* (top is at left; tape shows centimetres)

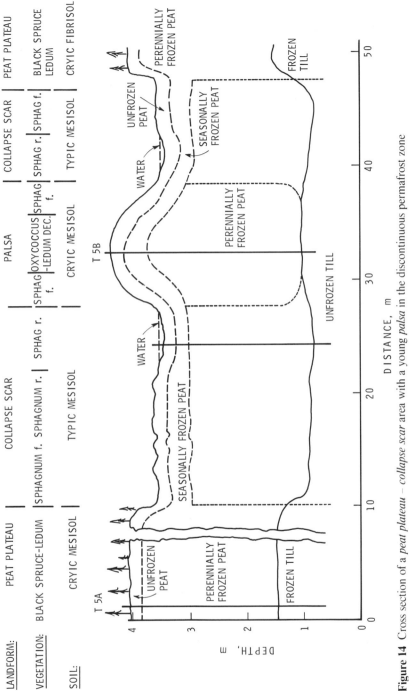

Figure 14 Cross section of a *peat plateau – collapse scar* area with a young *palsa* in the discontinuous permafrost zone (modified from Tarnocai, 1973)

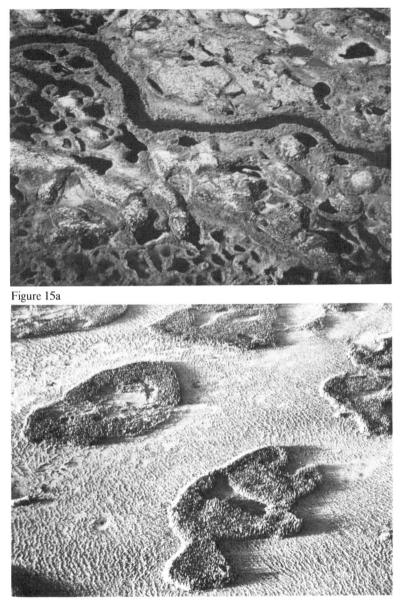

Figure 15a

Figure 15b

Figure 15 Examples of permafrost landforms developed in *peatlands*

(a) *Palsa* and *peat plateau* complex, Sheldrake Lake area, Quebec (Photo by M.K. Seguin, Université Laval)

(b) *Peat plateaus* occurring as islands in an unfrozen *string fen*, Nelson River area, Manitoba (Photo by S.C. Zoltai, Environment Canada)

Figure 15c

Figure 15d

Figure 15 (continued)

(c) *Polygonal peat plateau* near the tree line, Richardson Mountains, N.W.T.
(Photo by S.C. Zoltai, Environment Canada)

(d) A *string fen*, looking upstream, Lac La Ronge, Saskatchewan (Photo by S.C.
Zoltai, Environment Canada)

Figure 15 (continued)

(e) *Collapse scars*, some with remnant *peat plateaus* marked by tall trees, near Wabowden, Manitoba (Photo by S.C. Zoltai, Environment Canada)

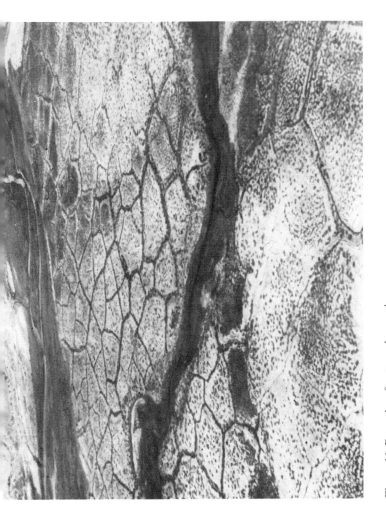

Figure 16 Examples of *patterned ground*

(a) Oblique aerial view of high-centre *polygons* on sediments of the Deer Bay Formation, northern Fosheim Peninsula, Ellesmere Island, N.W.T. (Photo by M.F. Nixon, Geological Survey of Canada)

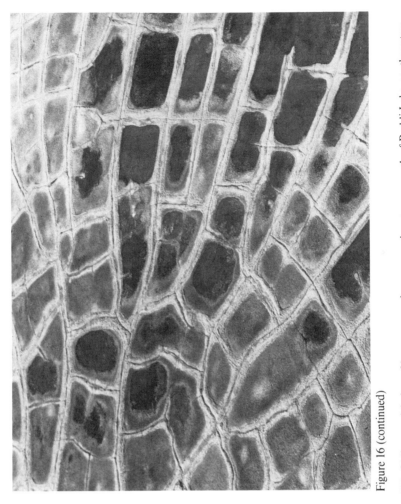

Figure 16 (continued)

(b) Oblique aerial view of low-centre *polygons* on a river terrace north of Raddi Lake, southwestern Banks Island, N.W.T. (Photo by J-S. Vincent, Geological Survey of Canada)

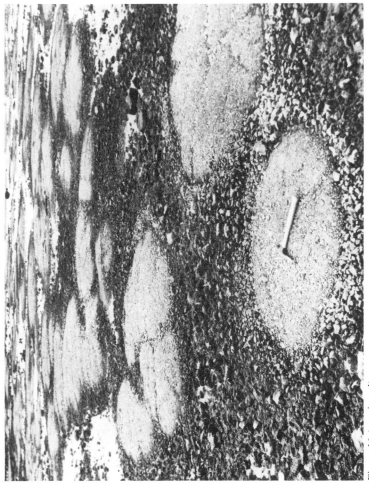

Figure 16 (continued)

(c) *Frost boils* on shallow lacustrine silts overlying till, on the west side of Irene Bay, central Ellesmere Island. N.W.T. (Photo by D.A. Hodgson, Geological Survey of Canada)

Figure 16 (continued)

(d) *Solifluction* of till across marine-limit raised beaches near Kaminak Lake, N.W.T. *Frost boils* can be seen on the till, thermal contraction crack *polygons* are seen on the raised beaches, and solifluction stripes are visible on the till in the middle-right of the field of view. The downslope edge of the solifluction sheet forms a turf-banked terrace. The white bar is the antenna of the helicopter. (Photo by W.W. Shilts, Geological Survey of Canada)

Figure 16 (continued)

(e) Non-sorted stripes in thin till overlying Cretaceous sandstones, eastern Banks Island, N.W.T. (Photo by H.M. French, University of Ottawa)

Figure 16 (continued)

(f) Sorted stripes on fissile sandstone of Jurassic age, near Mould Bay, Prince Patrick Island, N.W.T. (Photo by H.M. French, University of Ottawa)

Figure 17 *Ice, sand* and *soil wedges*

(a) *Ice wedge*, about 4 m wide at the top, in postglacial lake silts which overlie
truncated glacially deformed, ice-rich Pleistocene sediments more than
40,000 years old. Garry Island, N.W.T. (Photo by J.R. Mackay, University of
British Columbia)

143

Figure 17

(d) Rejuvenated *ice wedge* showing primary and secondary wedge exposed in coastal bluff 3 km west of Sachs Harbour, southern Banks Island, N.W.T. (Photo by H.M. French, University of Ottawa)

Figure 17

(c) Small syngenetic *ice wedge* formed in silty sand of late-Quaternary age, Sachs River lowlands, southern Banks Island, N.W.T. (Photo by D.G. Harry, Geological Survey of Canada)

Figure 17 (continued)

(b) Inactive *ice wedge* formed in silty clay, Sachs River lowlands, Southern Banks Island, N.W.T. (Photo by D.G. Harry, Geological Survey of

Figure 17e

Figure 17f

Figure 17 (continued)

(e) Epigenetic *ice wedge* exposed in coastal bluff 3 km west of Sachs Harbour, southern Banks Island, N.W.T. (Photo by D.G. Harry, Geological Survey of Canada)

(f) *Ice-wedge ice* showing foliated nature, southern Banks Island, N.W.T. (Photo by H.M. French, University of Ottawa)

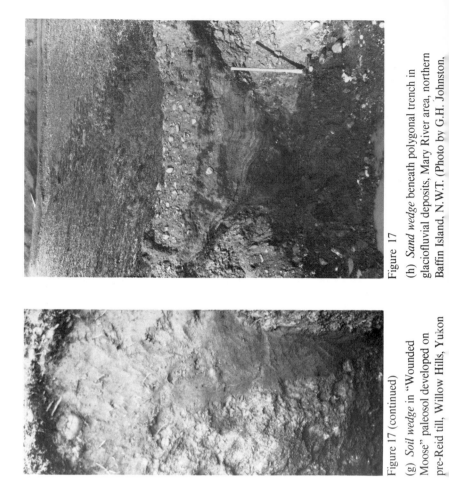

Figure 17 (continued)

(g) *Soil wedge* in "Wounded Moose" paleosol developed on pre-Reid till, Willow Hills, Yukon

Figure 17

(h) *Sand wedge* beneath polygonal trench in glaciofluvial deposits, Mary River area, northern Baffin Island, N.W.T. (Photo by G.H. Johnston.

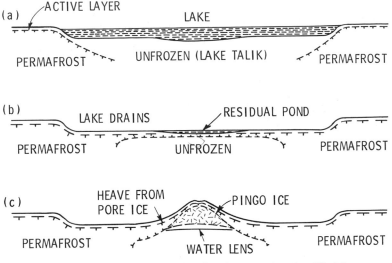

Figure 18 Illustration of the growth of a *closed-system pingo* (modified from Mackay, 1985)

Figure 19 *Pingos*

(a) A *closed-system pingo* (Ibyuk Pingo), 49 m high and 300 m in basal diameter, in the bottom of a drained lake near Tuktoyaktuk, N.W.T. The flats in the foreground are just above sea level and are flooded during storm surges. The pingo overburden is 15 m thick, the underlying sediments are sands and the pingo is still growing at the top at a rate of about 2 cm/year. (Photo by J.R. Mackay, University of British Columbia)

Figure 19b

Figure 19c

Figure 19 (continued)

(b) An *open-system pingo* on the alluvial fan in the Mala River Valley, Borden Peninsula, Baffin Island, N.W.T. (Photo by G.W. Scotter, Canadian Wildlife Service)

(c) A *pingo remnant* near Tuktoyaktuk, N.W.T. The basal diameter is about 300 m, which is almost identical with that of Ibyuk Pingo (see (a) above). The pond in the pingo is 5.4 m deep. The pingo probably grew at least several thousand years ago; the time of collapse is unknown. (Photo by J.R. Mackay, University of British Columbia)

Figure 20a

Figure 20b

Figure 20 Examples of *earth hummocks*

(a), (b) *Earth hummocks* near Inuvik, N.W.T., on a clay-silt colluvium, overlying
outwash gravels. Individual hummocks are 1 to 2 m in diameter, and the
troughs between the hummocks are 25 to 50 cm deep. Many hummocks
have exposed mineral soil on the top; the troughs are commonly filled
with moss and underlain by ice, year round. Figure 20(a) shows the
natural terrain, with an open woodland of black spruce and alder. Figure
20(b) shows the same area following a forest fire in 1968. (Photos by
H.M. French, University of Ottawa)

Figure 20c

Figure 20d

Figure 20 (continued)

(c) *Turf hummock* consisting of living and dead *Sphagnum fuscum*, District of Keewatin, N.W.T. (Photo by S.C. Zoltai, Environment Canada)

(d) *Thufa* in volcanic ash soils, Sunshine Meadows, near Banff, Alberta. (Photo by S.C. Zoltai, Environment Canada)

Figure 21a

Figure 21b

Figure 21 Examples of *mass wasting* in permafrost areas

(a) *Active-layer failure* in the upper Ramparts River area, Mackenzie Valley,
    N.W.T. (Photo by O.L. Hughes, Geological Survey of Canada)

(b) Active-layer detachment failure, Mackenzie Valley, N.W.T. (Photo by
    O.L. Hughes, Geological Survey of Canada)

Figure 21c

Figure 21d

Figure 21 (continued)

(c) *Retrogressive thaw slumping* in a borrow pit on the Dempster Highway near Ft. McPherson, N.W.T. (Photo by O.L. Hughes, Geological Survey of Canada)

(d) *Retrogressive thaw slumping* on the Yukon coastal plain near King Point, Yukon Territory. (Photo by J-S. Vincent, Geological Survey of Canada)

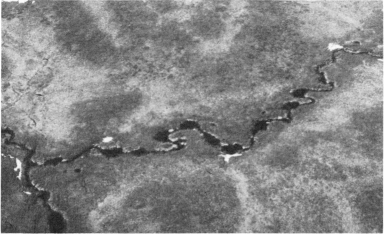

Figure 22a

Figure 22b

Figure 22 Examples of thermokarst features in permafrost areas

(a) *Beaded stream*, Mackenzie Delta area, N.W.T. (Photo by H.M. French, University of Ottawa)

(b) *Oriented lakes*, Bathurst Peninsula, N.W.T. The large lake in the foreground is 250 m long. The long axes of the lakes are oriented normal to the strongest prevailing summer wind. (Photo by J.R. Mackay, University of British Columbia)

Figure 22c

Figure 22d

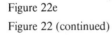

Figure 22e

Figure 22 (continued)

(c) *Thermokarst lake* showing shoreline erosion; shore of a typical expanding lake on overgrown pasture, west of Takhini River Crossing, Alaska Highway, Yukon Territory. (Photo by R.W. Klassen, Geological Survey of Canada)

(d) *Thermo-erosional niche* along the bank of the Rock River, Yukon Territory. (Photo by O.L. Hughes, Geological Survey of Canada)

(e) Fresh *thermokarst terrain* developing as a result of thawing of *ice wedges* in a borrow pit on the Dempster Highway near the crossing of the Blackstone River, Yukon Territory. (Photo by O.L. Hughes, Geological Survey of Canada)

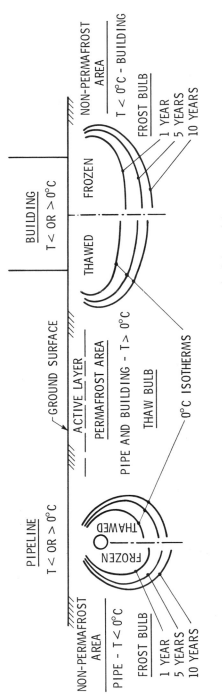

PIPELINE
T < OR > 0°C

BUILDING
T < OR > 0°C

NON-PERMAFROST
AREA
T < 0°C - BUILDING

FROST BULB

1 YEAR
5 YEARS
10 YEARS

FROZEN

THAWED

GROUND SURFACE

ACTIVE LAYER

PERMAFROST AREA

PIPE AND BUILDING - T > 0°C

THAW BULB

0°C ISOTHERMS

THAWED

FROZEN

NON-PERMAFROST
AREA
PIPE - T < 0°C

FROST BULB

1 YEAR
5 YEARS
10 YEARS

(Not to scale)

Figure 23 Illustration of the development of *frost* and *thaw bulbs* around buried pipelines and under buildings placed on the ground surface in permafrost and non-permafrost areas. For buildings, the diagram illustrates a cold structure in a non-permafrost area (e.g., an ice rink) and a warm structure in a permafrost area (e.g., a powerhouse). For pipelines, the diagram illustrates a chilled pipeline in a non-permafrost area and a warm pipeline in a permafrost area. In all cases the pipelines and buildings are operated at temperatures either above or below 0°C, continuously for several years.

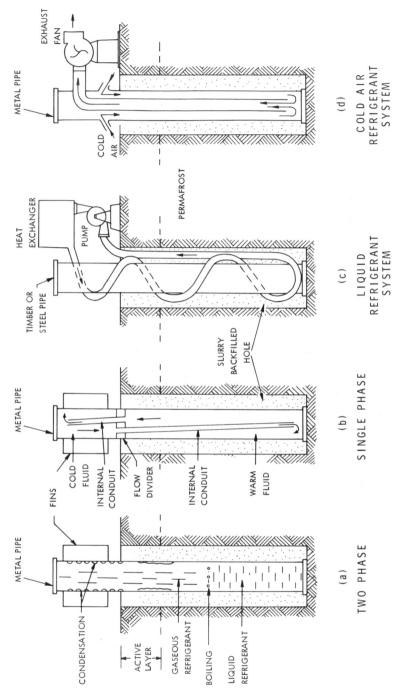

Figure 24 Representation of several *thermal pile* systems (after Johnston, 1981)